International Baccalaureate Physics Astrophysics Option D

For exams 2016 onwards

Introduction

Welcome to the International Baccalaureate Physics Guide to the Astrophysics Option. The author has 34 years teaching experience, 24 years of which has been spent teaching IB Physics in International Schools. The author studied Astronomy at University College London and followed this by working in the university's observatory at Mill Hill measuring Martian craters. During his teaching career he observed variable stars for AAVSO and recently helped proofread research papers for the Observatory of Nice about the surfaces of supergiant stars. Finally he wrote the previous two editions of the OSC Astrophysics booklet.

This guide is not a textbook, as it does not cover every syllabus statement in detail. Its aim is to support your textbook and notes made in class. This is achieved by summarising the key points and some two dozen worked examples each followed by similar problems. Also, there are several hands-on tasks allowing students to improve their graphing skills, a list of the commonest mistakes in the exam and finally over fifty questions-split into core and higher level extension, all with answers. Have a calculator at hand, plus pencil and eraser to fill in the spaces, have a go then rub out and try again at a later date.

I would like to thank Nicola Papworth for kindly proofreading the manuscript and many students for letting me use them as guinea pigs for the booklet.

I would greatly value any feedback on this revision guide so that later editions can continue to help students round the world. Please feel free to email me at Oxford Study Courses - (osc@osc-ib.com).

Hugh Duncan

Contents

D1 Stellar quantities

D1.1 Objects in the universe

The structure of the solar system

- The **solar system** is the collection of bodies that are gravitationally bound to the sun (planets, moons, asteroids and comets).
- The eight major **planets** constitute the major bodies in the solar system.
- They go round the sun in elliptical orbits (most are almost circular).
- In order of increasing distance from the sun, they are Mercury, Venus, Earth, Mars, Jupiter, Saturn, Uranus and Neptune.
- You can make up a mnemonic to remember the order e.g.:
  Most Very Eminent Men Just Sleep Under Newspapers (MVEMJSUN).
- In order of increasing size, they are Mercury, Mars, Venus, Earth, Uranus, Neptune, Saturn and Jupiter.
- Planets have a diameter of over 5000km.
- NOTE Pluto is no longer classed as a planet, but instead a **dwarf planet**.
- Dwarf planets include Ceres and some extra-Neptunian bodies, and tend to have a diameter of 1000-3000km.
- The **moons** or natural satellites orbit the planets.
- Between Mars and Jupiter there is a gap called the asteroid belt that is filled with many smaller bodies called **asteroids** or minor planets.
- Asteroids have diameters of 1 km up to several hundred km.
- There are other asteroid belts further out beyond Neptune.
- **Comets** are of a mixture of ice, dust and gas, just a few km across. Most comets orbit the sun in parabolic orbits, some elliptical, some hyperbolic.

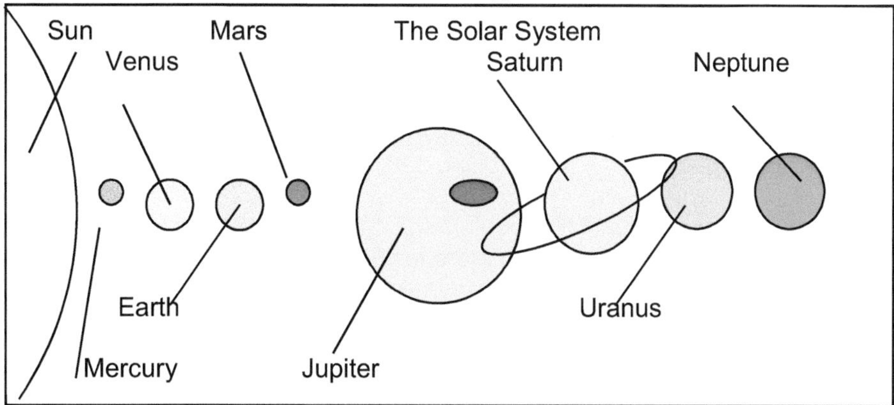

Name	Diameter/km	Orbit radius/AU	Period
Mercury	4800	0.4	88d
Venus	12000	0.7	224d
Earth	13000	1.0	1y
Mars	6700	1.5	1.9y
Jupiter	142000	5.0	12y
Saturn	120000	9.5	29y
Uranus	49000	19	84y
Neptune	50000	30	164y

- The solar system is an example of a **planetary system**.
- Over 400 planets have now been detected orbiting others stars.

Star groups

- A **galaxy** is a collection of 100 billion stars, dust and gas held together by gravity. They are normally **spiral** shaped or **elliptical**, but some are **irregular**. Our galaxy, the Milky Way is spiral.

- A **galactic cluster** is a collection of galaxies that are gravitationally bound.
- The Milky Way is part of a cluster of 20 galaxies called the **Local Group**.
- A collection of thousands of gravitationally bound galaxies is a **supercluster**.
- Within a galaxy a close group of bound stars is called a **cluster**. A **globular** cluster has about 10^5 stars symmetrically arranged and more densely packed in the centre. An **open** or moving cluster is irregular in shape with hundreds of stars. **Globular clusters** are old, **open clusters** are young.
- Stars in the same part of the sky (but may be at different distances), are grouped together into shapes called **constellations**.
- Consider distant street lights that make a pattern. They may be at different distances, but are in the same direction.
- The pair of diagrams below might help to show this. They each show the same constellation pattern of stars. However, if you cross your eyes and allow one image to merge with the other (this is a stereogram a bit like Magic Eye), it can be seen that one of the stars is further away than the others. Have a go!

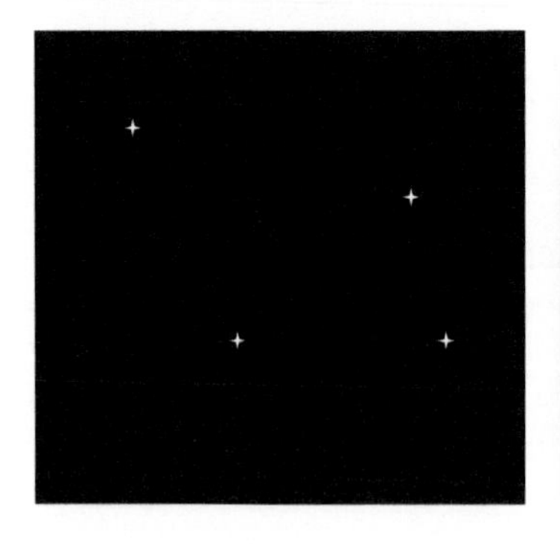
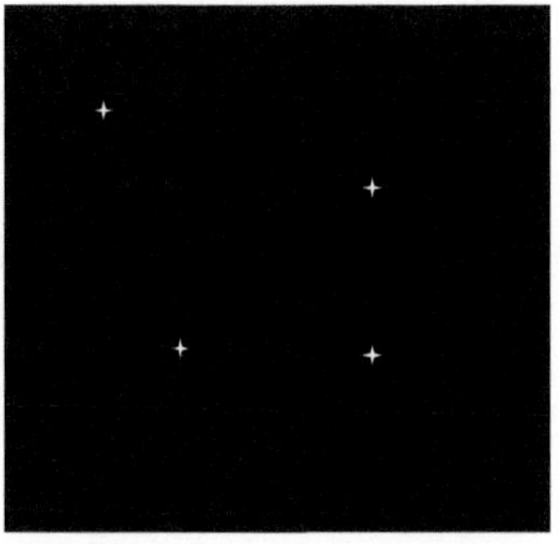

- N.B. it's the top left one. Bottom right is nearest. If the stars weren't so far away or if our eyes were very far apart, we'd be able to see them at different distances!

Types of stars

Single: a star that is not bound by gravity to another, such as the sun.
Binary: two stars that appear close together in the sky and may be physically related.
Cepheid: a star that varies in brightness over a period of days, due to changes in size.
Red Giant: a star that has finished hydrogen burning and is using helium in the core. Very large with a low surface temperature.
Supergiant: a star heavy enough that fusion takes place for elements beyond carbon.
White Dwarf: a star of solar mass but planetary size with no more fusion energy, only gravitational.
Optical binary: two stars close together in the sky, but not close in space.
Visual binary: two stars that orbit one another (gravitationally bound).
Eclipsing binary: stars orbiting each other- one passes in front of the other.

Task 1: put these in increasing size: Jupiter, galaxy, Ceres, open cluster.

Key points
The solar system is all the bodies gravitationally bound to the sun.
Moons orbit planets which orbit the sun (or other stars).
Galaxies are gravitationally bound groups of billions of stars.

D1.2 The nature of stars

- The source of energy for the stars comes from **nuclear fusion**.
- Four hydrogen nuclei collide at speed to form helium (*see later*).
- Energy is released in the form of radiation.
- The force of gravity is trying to collapse a star.
- The radiation created in nuclear fusion exerts an outward pressure on a star.
- The two forces of gravity and radiation pressure are in equilibrium, making a star stable.
- A mass hanging at rest on a spring is a useful analogy:

- The downward force is gravity on the mass: its weight.
- This is balanced by an equal upward force, the tension in the spring.
- Note, if the mass is given a small push, it will bounce up and down.
- This analogy will be useful when considering Cepheid variable stars later.
- Another analogy would be a shooting game at the fun fair:
  - Jets of water or air are directed upwards.
  - Ping pong balls are made to float on these jets.
  - The weight of the balls is balanced by the force of the jets on them.
  - As the jets are not constant, the balls wobble, making them hard to hit.

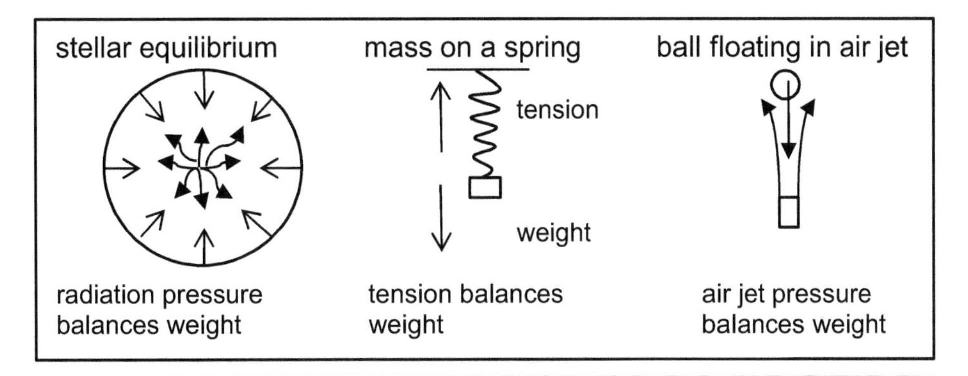

Task 2: what is formed with the fusion of four hydrogen nuclei?

Key points
A star's energy source is fusion.
Radiation pressure balances weight to make a stable star.

D1.3 Astronomical distances

The Astronomical Unit

- The **astronomical unit** (AU) is the mean earth sun distance.
- It is given in the data book as 1AU = 1.5×10^{11}km.
- It is a convenient unit for distances in the solar system and nearby stars.

The planetary distances in the table on page 3 are given in AU.
What is the radius of Mercury's orbit in km?

$r = 0.4$ AU $= 0.4 \times 1.5 \times 10^{11}$ = 60 million km

Work out the other planetary distances in metres.

The light year

- A **light year** is the distance light travels in one year, unit ly.
- The speed of light is 3.0×10^{8} ms^{-1}, given in the data book.
- to find the distance light travels in a year:
  - there are 365 days in a year, 24 hrs a day, 60 mins an hour and 60 sec a minute
  - a light year is equal to:

  1 ly = $3 \times 10^{8} \times 365 \times 24 \times 60 \times 60 = 9.46 \times 10^{15}$ m
- This value is given in the data book.

How many AU make a light year? Confirm that it is about 63 000.

Task 3:
1. The moon is 370 000 km away. How long does it take light to travel from the earth to the moon? Note c is 300 000kms^{-1}.
2. How far away is the sun in light minutes if the distance is 150 000 000km?
3. The closest star after the sun is Proxima Centauri, 4.3ly away. How far is this in metres? The fastest man-made object reached 150 000 ms^{-1}. How long would it take for it to travel to Proxima Centauri in years?

4. The most distant star visible to the naked eye is Epsilon Aurigi at 5000ly. How far is this in metres?
5. The most distant galaxy visible to the naked eye is the Andromeda Galaxy M31 at 2.2×10^6 ly. How far is this in metres?

- Another useful distance unit in astrophysics is the **parsec** (unit pc).
- It is defined below but in brief 1pc = 3.26 ly. It is in the data book.

How many AU in a parsec? How many metres in a parsec? 206 000AU. 3.08×10^{16}m
The Milky Way is 150 000ly across. How many parsecs is this? 46kpc.

Key points
An astronomical unit is the mean earth sun distance.
A light year is the distance light travels in a year.

D1.4 Stellar Parallax

Hold your finger up at arms-length in front of your face. Close one eye and look at the finger, and then do the same with the other eye. Your finger appears to move against the background. This is known as **parallax**: the apparent movement of a nearby object against the background as seen from two positions. Take the earth in two positions on its orbit, six months apart. A nearby star is observed on those two dates (see diagram). Its position relative to the distant stars will change. The **angle of parallax**, p is the difference in angular positions as seen from the earth and sun, measured in seconds of arc. The closer the star, the larger the parallax.

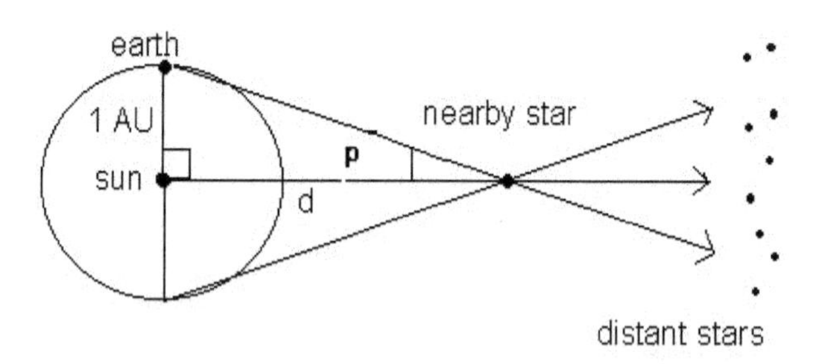

A **parsec** is the distance at which a star has a parallax of 1 second of arc.
The distance d in parsecs pc is $d = \frac{1}{p}$, with the parallax angle in arc seconds.

Worked example:
Our closest neighbouring star system, α Centauri, has a parallax of 0.760 arc seconds. Using the triangle in the diagram, with the earth-sun distance as 1 AU, this makes the distance to the nearest star (one degree is 60 minutes and one minute is 60 seconds, so one arc second is therefore ${}^{1}/_{3600}$ of a degree) as:
opposite / adjacent = tangent, so adjacent = opposite / tangent
$d = {}^{1\text{AU}}/_{\tan(0.76\text{ arc sec})}$ which is about 271 000 AU. What is this in metres? Find 1AU in the data book. In light years? Find 1ly in data book! (Answer: 4.1×10^{16}km, or 4.3 ly)

Worked example:
The nearest star has a parallax of 0.760 arc sec. What is this in parsecs?
Use $d=\frac{1}{p}$, so $d=\frac{1}{0.76}$, d = 1.3pc.

- This method can only be used for stars within 100pc.
- Beyond this, parallax is so small that the error is too large.

Task 4: what is the distance when the parallax is 0.010 arc sec? 0.002 arc sec? If the error in parallax is ±0.001 arc sec, what error does this give for these distances?

Key points
A parsec is the distance at which a star has a parallax of one arc sec.
This distance method can be used out to 100pc.

D1.5 Stellar radiation and stellar types

- **Luminosity** is the total power output of a star in watts.
- The luminosity of a 100W light bulb is 100W! That is 100 Joules per second.
- The luminosity of the sun is 3.9×10^{26} W.
- The **apparent brightness** is the power output per unit area at a given distance and is measured in Wm^{-2}.
- If a star of luminosity L (W) is observed from a distance:
  d (m), then the apparent brightness b (Wm^{-2}) is given by

$$b = \frac{L}{4\pi d^2}$$

As an example, suppose you are standing 3m away from a 100W light bulb. Its apparent brightness given by the equation will be

$$b = \frac{100}{4 \times 3.14 \times 3^2} = 0.9\ Wm^{-2}$$

Worked example:
Using the luminosity figure for the sun as 3.9×10^{26} W, its brightness as seen from the earth, at a distance of 1.5×10^{11}m can be found:
$L = 3.9\times10^{26}$ W
$d = 1.5 \times 10^{11}$m

$$b = \frac{3.9 \times 10^{26}}{4 \times 3.14 \times (1.5 \times 10^{11})^2}$$

$b = 1379Wm^{-2} = 1400Wm^{-2}$ (2 sig fig) Note this figure is known as the **solar constant.**

Task 5: What would the apparent brightness of the sun be at a distance of one light year?

Black body radiation

- A **black body** is a perfect absorber and a perfect emitter of radiation.
- A star is an example of an object close to being a black body.
- The relative amounts of each type of radiation from a black body depend only on the surface temperature of the black body.
- Below is a graph showing the intensity of radiation for three black bodies at different temperatures. The vertical axis is an arbitrary intensity unit; the horizontal axis is wavelength in nm. As the surface temperature increases:
  - There is an increase in all types of radiation.
  - There is a greater increase for shorter wavelength radiation.
  - The peak of intensity shifts to shorter wavelengths.

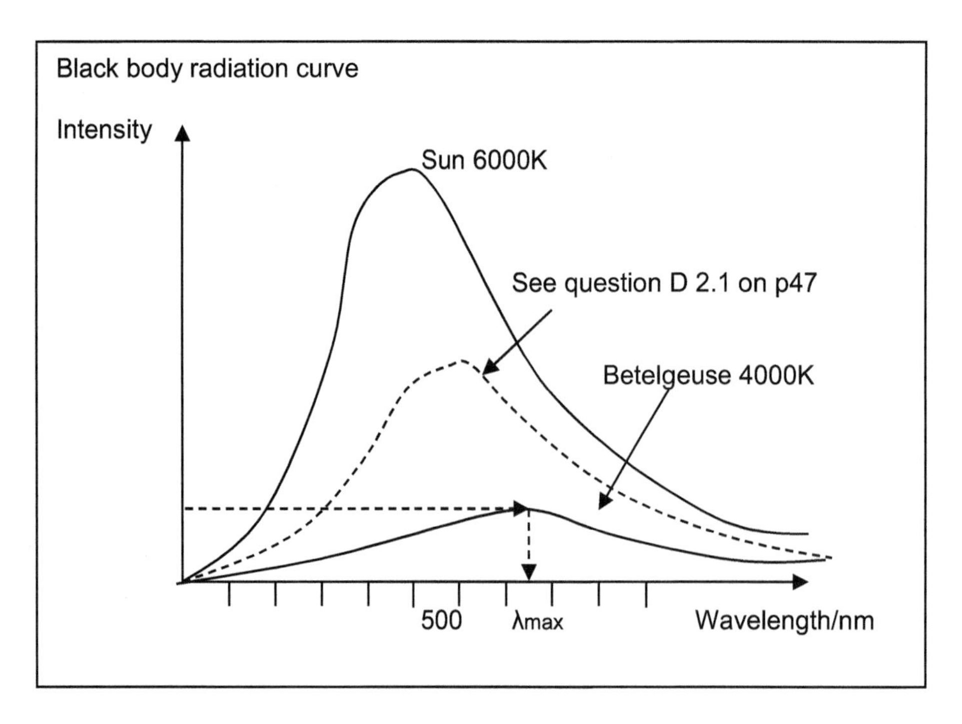

Wien's Law and the Stefan-Boltzmann Law

Wien's Displacement Law states that the wavelength at peak intensity for a black body is inversely proportional to the surface temperature.
wavelength at max intensity = constant ÷ temperature

$$\lambda_{max} = \frac{0.00290}{T}$$

where λ is in m and T is the temperature in Kelvin.

Worked example
The constant in Wien's law is 0.00290 Kelvin-metres (Km). If the spectrum of Betelgeuse peaks at 700nm, the quoted surface temperature can be found:
Constant = 0.00290 Km
Wavelength at max intensity = 700nm (change to metres!) = 7×10^{-7}m
Rearrange formula temp = constant ÷ peak wavelength
Temp = $0.00290 \div 7 \times 10^{-7}$m = 4142 = 4100K (2sf)
Using the wavelength at max intensity found earlier for the sun (500nm), calculate the surface temperature; (Ans 5800K 2sf)

- The luminosity of a star is proportional to its surface area.
- The luminosity of a star is proportional to the fourth power of the surface temperature. This is called **Stefan-Boltzmann's Law.**
- For two different sized stars of the same temperature, the power output per unit area is the same.
- The radiation rate is L (known as the power or luminosity) in watts.
- The surface temperature is T in Kelvin.
- The surface area is A in m^2.
- The Stefan-Boltzmann formula is:

$$L = \sigma A T^4$$

σ is Stefan's constant 5.7×10^{-8} $Wm^{-2}K^{-1}$.

Worked example:
Take the sun, where T = 6000K and its radius is 6.7×10^{8} m. Find the power output.
T = 6000K $A = 4 \times \pi \times (6.7 \times 10^{8})^2 = 5.64 \times 10^{18}$ m²
$\sigma = 5.7 \times 10^{-8}$ W/m²/K
$L = 5.7 \times 10^{-8} \times 5.64 \times 10^{18} \times 6000^4 = 4.29 \times 10^{26}$ W $= 4.3 \times 10^{26}$ W (2sf)
(Note this is approximately the number given earlier).

Task 6: Sirius has a surface temperature of 13000K and a radius of 1.3×10^{9} m. Find the power output.

Key points
A black body is a perfect emitter and absorber.
Luminosity is the power output of a star.
Apparent brightness is the power per unit area as seen from earth.
The wavelength at peak intensity is inversely related to the star's temperature.

Exam Question 1: fill in the missing words numbered below into the spaces, then check the answers on the next page.

Can you name (1) the collection of bodies bound by gravity to the sun. (2) the smallest planet. (3) the furthest planet from the sun. (4) bodies that orbit the planets. (5) bodies found orbiting between Mars and Jupiter. (6) small bodies made of dust, gas and ice. (7) a large collection of stars bound by gravity, which can be either (8), (9), or (10). (11) a large symmetrical collection of stars in a galaxy. (12) a small irregular collection of stars in a galaxy. (13) a set of stars making a pattern, seemingly close in the sky. (14) the distance light travels in a year. (15) the source of energy for stars. (16) the power output in watts. (17) the power output per unit area at a given distance. (18) a perfect absorber and emitter of radiation. (19) law: the wavelength at peak intensity of the black body source is inversely related to surface temperature. (20) law: the luminosity of a star depends on the fourth power of the surface temperature. (21) star: a star not bound by gravity to another. (22) star: two stars bound by gravity. (23) an unstable star that goes through periodic changes in brightness. (24) a star burning helium, the outer layers have expanded and cooled. (25) a star the size of the earth that has no fusion energy left, only gravitational. (26) binary: two stars close together in the sky. (27) binary: two stars bound by gravity and seen as two objects.

1.	2.	3.	4.	5.	6.	7.	8.	9.
10.	11.	12.	13.	14.	15.	16.	17.	18.
19.	20.	21.	22.	23.	24.	25.	26.	27.

D1 Answers

Task 1: Ceres, Jupiter, Open cluster, Galaxy
Task 2: Helium nuclei
Task 3:1. 1.2s
2. 8.3min
3. 4.1×10^{16} m, 8600yrs!
4. 4.73×10^{19} m
5. 2.1×10^{22} m
Task 4: 100±10pc, 500 +500 or -200pc. NB error grows rapidly with distance.
Task 5: 3.5×10^{-7} Wm^{-2}. Use $b = L/4\pi d^2$
Task 6: 3.5×10^{28} W. Use $L = \sigma A T^4$

Exam Question 1 Answers:

1. solar system	2. mercury	3. Neptune
4. moons / satellites	5. minor planets / asteroids	6. comets
7. galaxy	8. spiral	9. elliptical
10. irregular	11. globular cluster	12. open/ moving cluster
13. constellation	14. light year	15. fusion
16. luminosity	17. brightness	18. black body
19. Wein's	20. Stefan's	21. single
22. binary	23. Cepheid	24. red giant
25. white dwarf	26. Optical	27. visual

D2 Stellar characteristics and Stellar evolution

D2.1 Stellar Spectra

- A pure gaseous element gives out very specific wavelengths of EM radiation when heated or excited by a voltage. If spread out an **emission line spectrum** is seen.
- A black body gives out radiation of all wavelengths. A **continuous spectrum** is seen when this is split up with a prism or diffraction grating.
- If a continuous spectrum is shone through a gaseous element, the colours the element would normally give out are absorbed and dark lines appear.
- Stars are not perfect black bodies as their thin atmospheres absorb certain colours and leave dark lines in the spectrum.
- Each element absorbs an individual set of colours, so the dark lines in a star's spectrum allow the chemical composition of a star to be found.
- Some physical properties of a star can be found with the spectrum.
- If the lines are blue shifted or red shifted (see later) then the star's motion towards or away from us can be determined.
- Light from a hot wire bulb can be observed through a prism or diffraction grating, and a complete spectrum is seen, called a **continuous emission spectrum**.
- A discharge tube contains a gaseous element at low pressure. If a high voltage is applied (e.g. 5kV), it glows and the spectrum is observed. The spectrum is not continuous, but contains discrete **emission lines**.
- Emission lines depend only on the element in the discharge tube.
- If a continuous spectrum is shone through a discharge tube that is not connected to 5kV, dark lines appear in the continuous spectrum. This is called an **absorption line spectrum**.
- All three spectra are shown below, including intensity (I)-wavelength graphs.

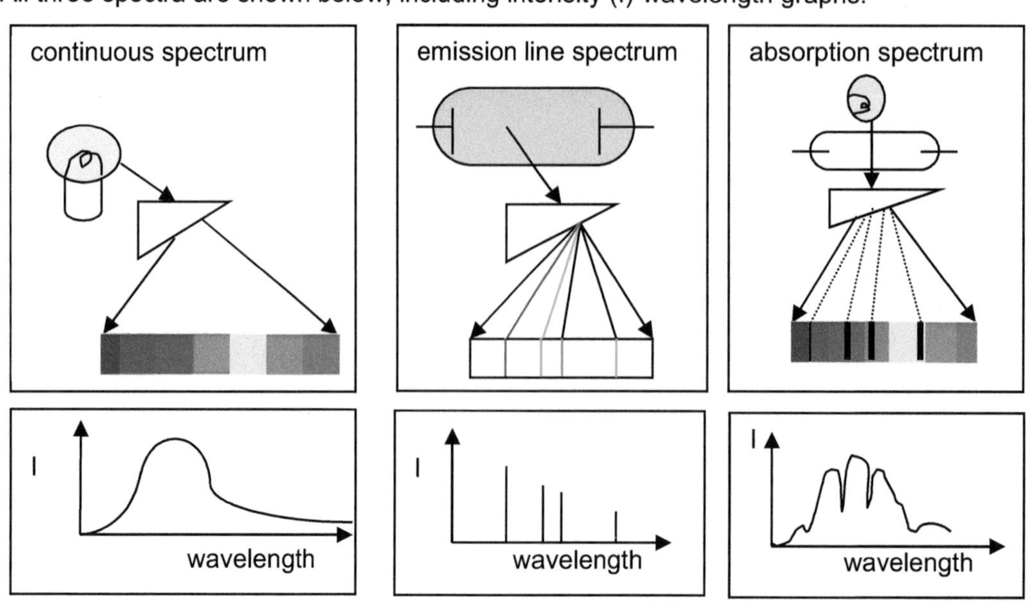

Task 7: name the device other than the prism that is used to split light to study spectra.

Key points
Gases at low pressure when excited give out emission line spectra.
When a continuous spectrum shines through a low pressure gas an absorption spectrum is created.
All other materials when excited give out continuous emission spectra.

D2.2 The Hertzsprung-Russell Diagram

- Stars that have the same colour have the same surface temperature.
- Stars of the same colour have the same power output per unit area.
- Stars of the same temperature can be very different in size (a red supergiant and red dwarf for example).
- A graph of a star's luminosity against its surface temperature is called a **Hertzsprung-Russell diagram** (HR diagram), see below.
  - The y-axis is numbered either in Watts or in terms of the sun's luminosity.
  - The x-axis represents temperature, and shows decreasing temperature.
  - The scales on an HR diagram are logarithmic rather than linear.
  - Blue is the hottest colour at 50 000K and red is the coolest at 3 000K.

The IB have dropped spectral type from the syllabus, but it will still be encountered in books, previous IB notes, papers and web sites. The IB have also dropped apparent and absolute magnitude, which are used to indicate brightness and luminosity. They will still be encountered in books, previous IB papers and websites.

Task 8: from the table, plot each star onto the blank HR diagram on the next page, with luminosity relative to the sun against the surface temperature, which remember is plotted backwards!

Star	Temp	Lum
61 Cyg	4 000	0.036
Aldebaren	4 400	160
α Centauri A	5 800	1.4
α Centauri B	4 600	0.44
Altair	7 900	10
Ankaa	5 200	69
Archenar	15 000	630
Barnards Star	3 200	0.00044
Betelgeuse	M2	23 000
Delta Cephi*	6 500	23 000
Enif	5 000	5 700
Eta Cas b	3 800	0.028
Kruger 60	3 500	0.0014
LP656-2	4 400	0.000048
Menkar	3 600	160
Eta Oph	38 000	2 800
Alnitak	38 000	23 000
Rigel	12 000	52 000
Beta Aur	9 000	100
O Eri b	8 300	0.0030
Caph	7 100	21
Scutulum	7 400	5 200
Eta Psc	5 400	110
115636	4 400	4 800
Scheat	3 600	300

Star	Temp	Lum
Mintaka	38 000	23000
Mira	3 100	210
Mirach	3 800	76
Naos	54 000	630
Polaris*	6 300	580
ProcyonB	6 800	0.00052
Procyon A	6 700	7.6
Proxima	3 200	0.000053
Sirius A	9 300	23
Sirius B	8 300	0.0016
Spica	23 000	1 700
Suhail	4 400	5 200
Tau ceti	5 400	0.40
Wolf 28	5 800	0.00016
Wolf 359	2 700	0.000017
Gamma Vel	54 000	8 300
Alpheratz	11 00	190
Alnilam	29 000	40 000
Deneb	9 000	69000
L145-141	7 800	0.000052
Wezen	6 300	69 000
σ Pavo	5 600	1.0
36 Oph	5 100	0.23
Antares	3 700	4 800
1326	3 700	160

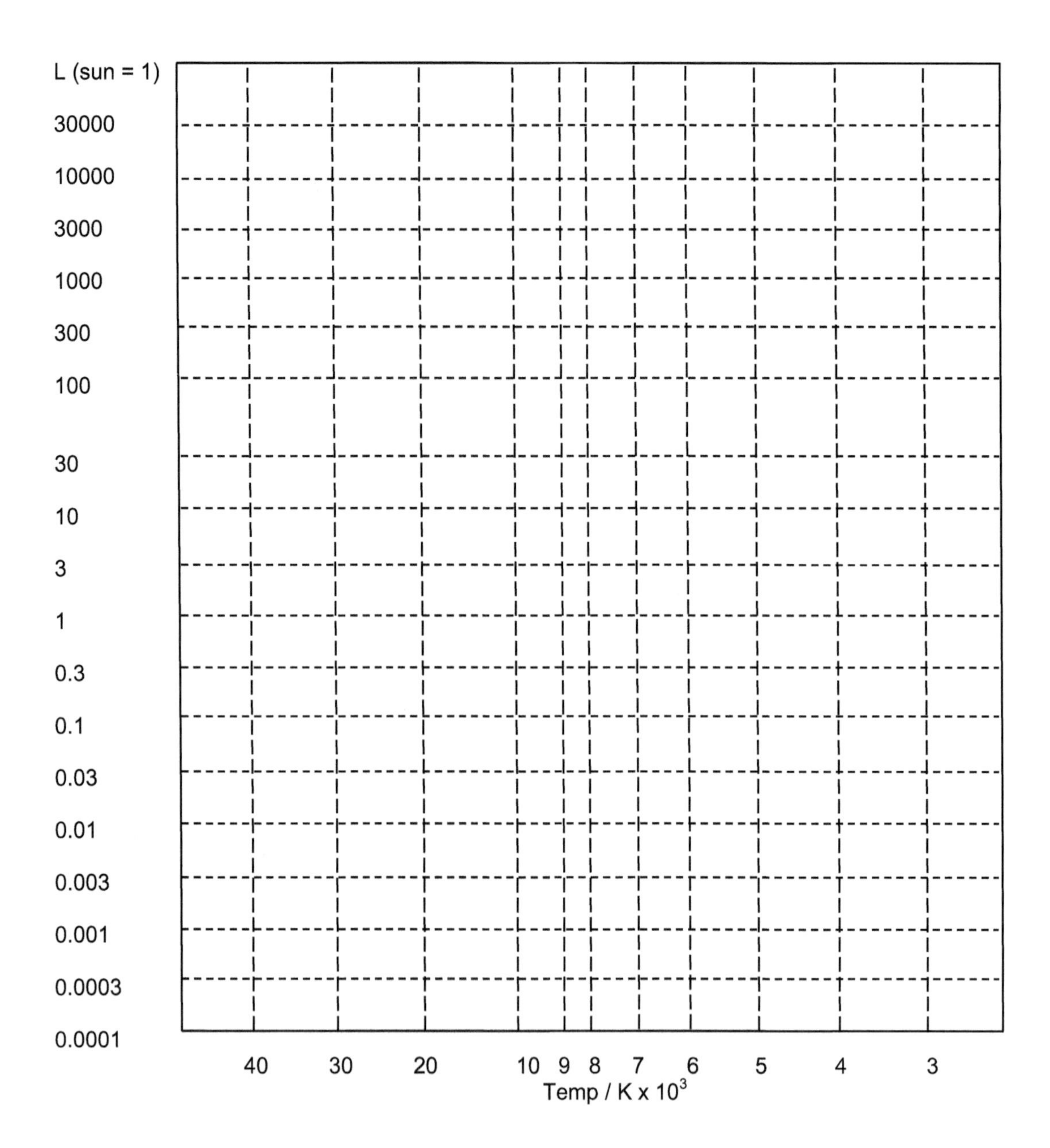

The main features of the diagram are:

- The **Main Sequence** (MS) runs from top left to bottom right.
  - MS stars show a direct relationship between absolute magnitude (luminosity) and surface temperature.
  - The sun is near the centre of the main sequence.
  - MS stars are burning hydrogen by nuclear fusion to helium.
  - Heavier MS stars burn faster, look brighter, are hotter and bluer.
  - Lighter MS stars burn slower, are fainter, cooler, and look red.
  - A star's position on the main sequence depends on its mass, from 0.2 solar masses for the red end to 20+ solar masses or more for the blue end.
- **Red Giants** stars have used up the hydrogen in their cores.
  - Their cores have contracted and heated up so helium fusion can take place.
  - The triple alpha process creates carbon (see later).
  - The outer layers expand and cool, turning red, hence the name.
  - Red giants are larger, more luminous and higher up on the HR diagram.
- **Supergiant** stars have used up the helium in their cores.
  - Their cores have contracted, heated up and carbon fusion starts.
  - The outer layers expand, helium fusion continues in an outer shell.

- They are larger than the giants, more luminous and higher on the diagram.

- **Cepheids** stars are giants that go through a period of instability.
  - They oscillate in size, and change temperature and luminosity.
  - They are found between the main sequence and the giants in a space known as the instability trip.
- **White dwarfs** have no more nuclear fuel.
  - Gravity has overcome the radiation pressure contracting that star, heating up by converting gravitational energy to radiation.
  - They are earth-sized, faint and found below the main sequence.
- Note that the sun's evolution can be shown on the HR diagram.

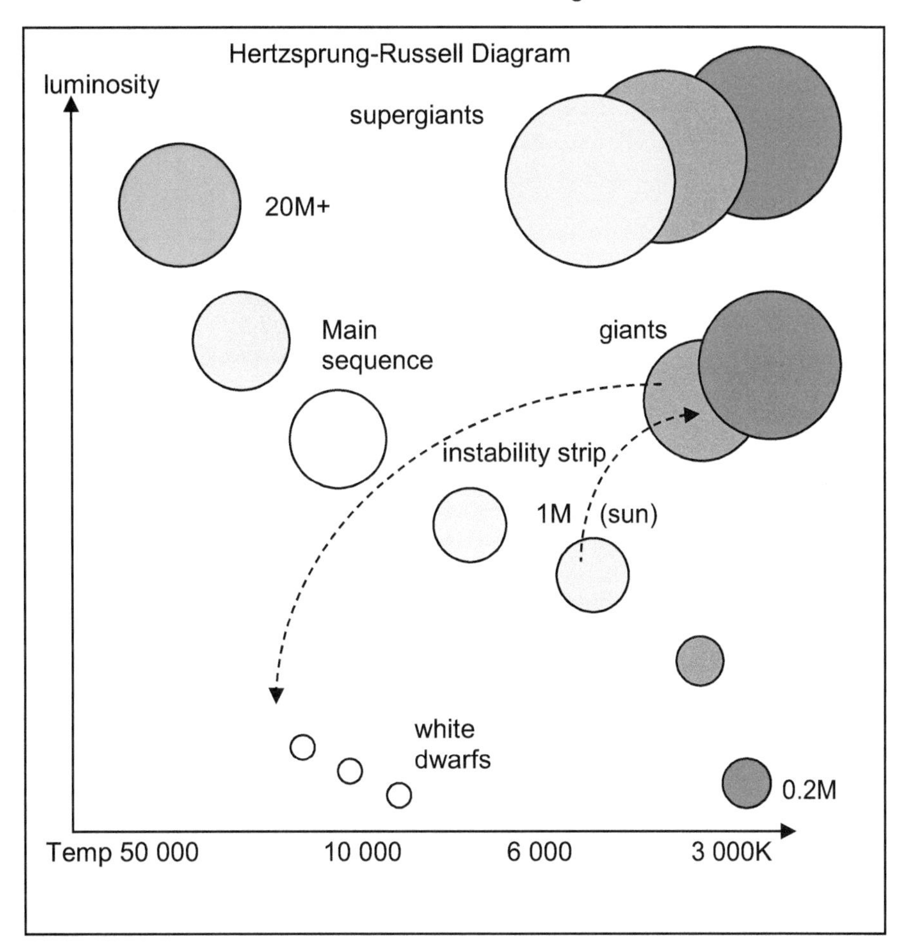

Key point
A Hertzsprung Russell diagram is a plot of a star's luminosity and surface temperature. It allows identification of the main stellar types.

D2.3 Mass-Luminosity Relation of Main Sequence Stars

Activity: calculate the log of the stars' luminosities and masses and complete the table to 2dp. Then plot the points on the graph shown below. What kind of relationship is there between the mass of a star and its luminosity?

Name of star	Lum	Log Lum	mass M sun = 1	log M
Sun	1.0		1.0	
Eta Cas A	0.83		0.85	
Eta Cas B	0.027		0.52	
UV Cet	0.00004		0.035	
o² Cet	0.33		0.8	
C	0.00069		0.21	
Sirius	23		2.3	
Procyon	6.9		1.8	

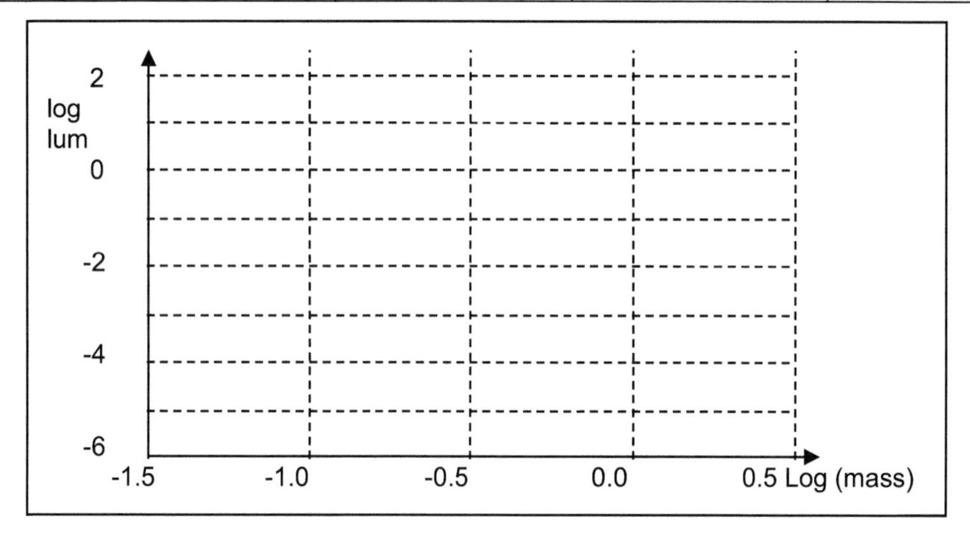

- The luminosity of a star depends on its mass.
- The greater the mass, the greater the luminosity.

If L is the star's luminosity compared to the sun and M is the mass in terms of the solar mass then

$$\log L = 3.5 \log M$$

Or putting it another way

$$L = M^{3.5}$$

So a star twice the mass of the sun will have a luminosity $2^{3.5}$ or about 11 times as luminous.
A star that is 20 times the mass of the sun will be $20^{3.5}$ as luminous or about 36 000 times as bright.

- The symbol $\odot$ is used when we are describing a quantity compared to that of the sun. e.g. $L_{\odot}$ = luminosity of the sun.

Task 9: Mintaka has a mass 17.6 times the sun. Find its luminosity. 61 Cyg has a luminosity 1/28 that of the sun's. Find the mass of 61 Cyg in solar masses.

Key points
A main sequence star's luminosity depends on the mass.
Luminosity is proportional to $Mass^{3.5}$.

D2.4 Cepheid variables

- A **Cepheid** variable is a star that varies in brightness over a period of days, due to changes in size and power output.
- They are named after the most famous one: Delta Cephei.
- A graph of the magnitude against time for a star is called its **light curve.**

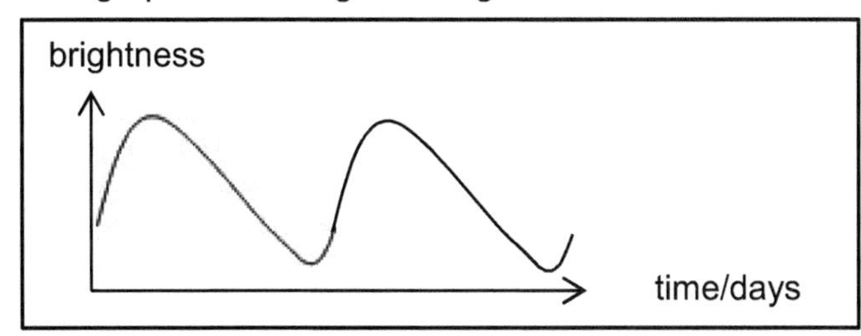

- Delta Cephei changes in brightness by about a factor two. This repeats on a cycle of every five days or so.
- Cepheids are above the Main Sequence, and yellow/orange in colour.
- They vary in temperature around 5-6 000K.
- They vary in temperature and luminosity as they vary in radius.
- Cepheids are used to determine distance.
- The more luminous the Cepheid, the longer its period.
- The relationship between luminosity and period is not linear and needs a log graph to illustrate the pattern as a straight line.

Activity: a cepheid with a period of 2 days has a luminosity of $650L_{\odot}$, while one with a period of 50 days has a luminosity of $20\ 000L_{\odot}$. Plot these two points onto the blank log graph below and join them with a straight line. It's only approximate, don't worry!

Graph of period luminosity for cepheid variables

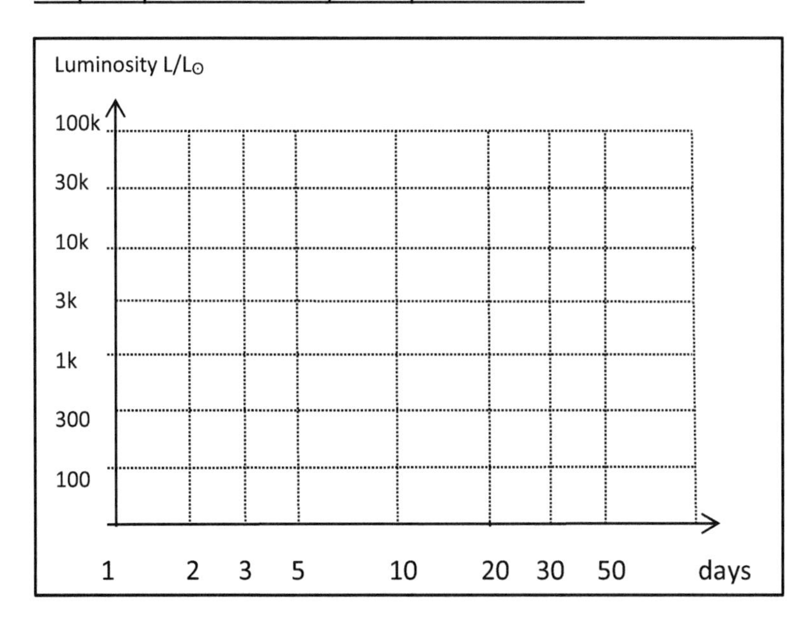

Worked example: Delta Cephi has a period of five days and a mean brightness of 3.3×10^{-14} $b_{\odot}$. Find its luminosity and distance.
Use period = 5 days, then read L off the graph. A period of 5 days gives $L \approx 1500\ L_{\odot}$ Use $d = \sqrt{L/4\pi b}$ so $d=\sqrt{1500/4 \times 3.14 \times 3.3\ \times 10^{-14}}$ = $6\text{x}10^{7}$AU about 950ly or 290pc.

Task 10: Zeta Gem has a period of 10 days and brightness of $2.9\text{x}10^{-13}$ $b_{\odot}$. Find the luminosity and distance. A Cepheid in a galaxy has a brightness of $9.8\text{x}10^{-21}$ $b_{\odot}$ and a period of 2.5 days. How far away is it?

Cause of Cepheid Variability

Cepheids are stars passing through an instability phase. The cycle repeats over a regular period of days. A star that has enough helium, such as a giant that has left the main sequence, can undergo this type of oscillation. The cause for the cycle is shown in the flow chart below. NOTE: the yellow/orange colours of the boxes in the cycle reflect the colour changes of a cepheid as it varies.

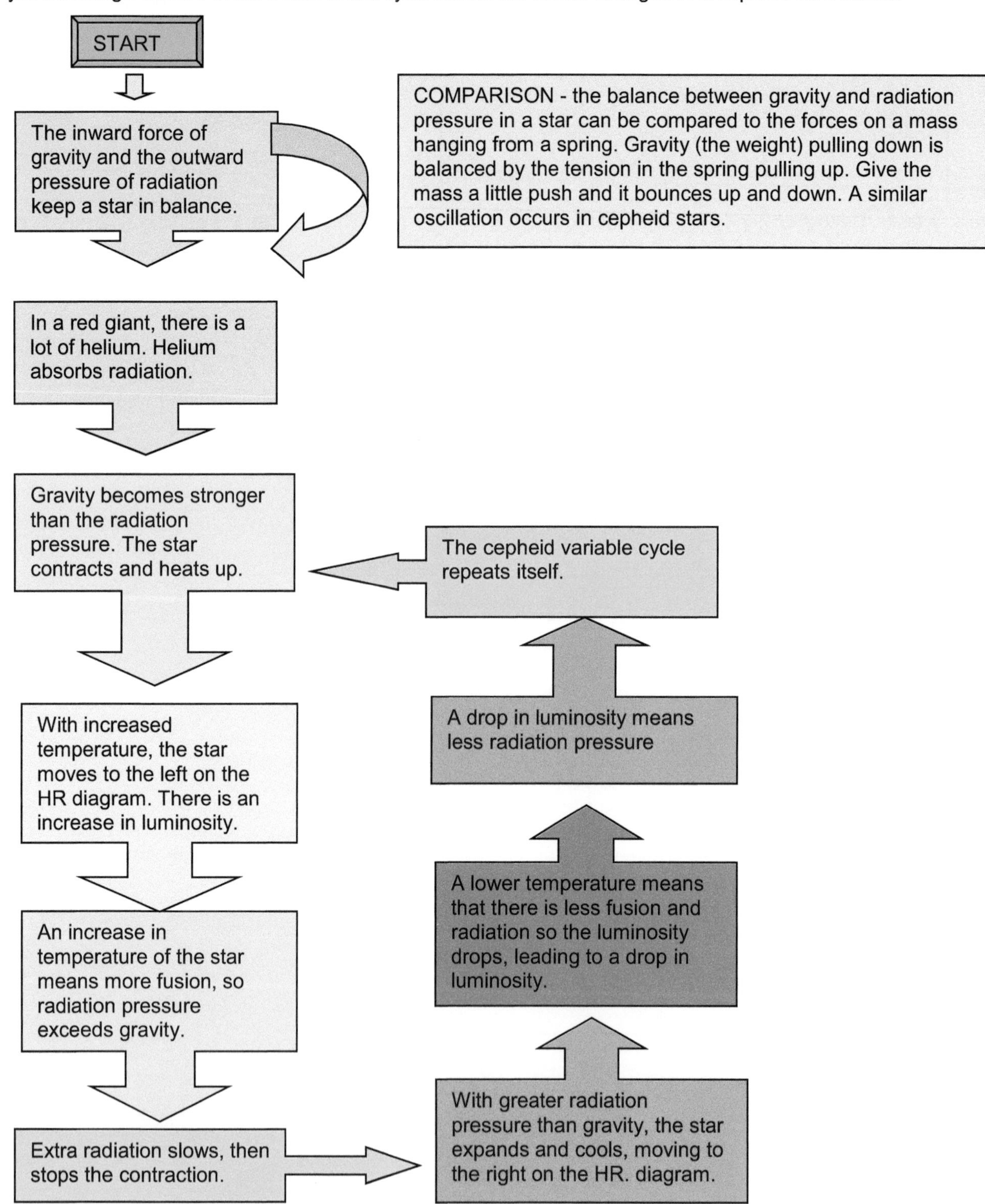

START
The inward force of gravity and the outward pressure of radiation keep a star in balance.
COMPARISON - the balance between gravity and radiation pressure in a star can be compared to the forces on a mass hanging from a spring. Gravity (the weight) pulling down is balanced by the tension in the spring pulling up. Give the mass a little push and it bounces up and down. A similar oscillation occurs in cepheid stars.
In a red giant, there is a lot of helium. Helium absorbs radiation.
Gravity becomes stronger than the radiation pressure. The star contracts and heats up.
With increased temperature, the star moves to the left on the HR diagram. There is an increase in luminosity.
An increase in temperature of the star means more fusion, so radiation pressure exceeds gravity.
Extra radiation slows, then stops the contraction.
With greater radiation pressure than gravity, the star expands and cools, moving to the right on the HR. diagram.
A lower temperature means that there is less fusion and radiation so the luminosity drops, leading to a drop in luminosity.
A drop in luminosity means less radiation pressure
The cepheid variable cycle repeats itself.

Practise Question: The cepheid variable cycle flow chart has been reproduced below, with many of the key words missing. Fill in the blank spaces without looking at the original diagram and then go back and check them. Good luck!

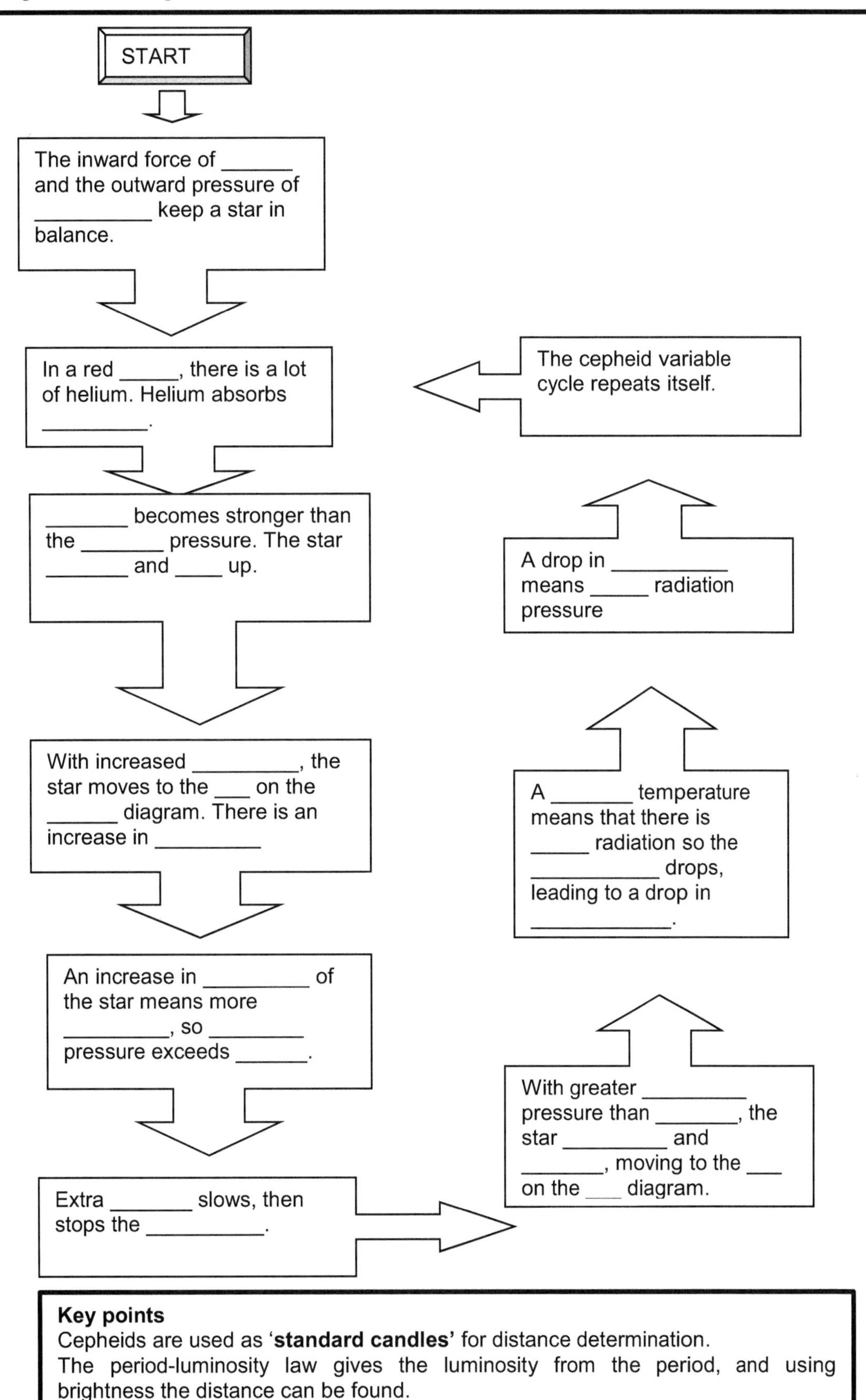

START
The inward force of ______ and the outward pressure of __________ keep a star in balance.
In a red _____, there is a lot of helium. Helium absorbs _________.
_______ becomes stronger than the _______ pressure. The star _______ and ____ up.
With increased _________, the star moves to the ___ on the ______ diagram. There is an increase in _________
An increase in _________ of the star means more _________, so ________ pressure exceeds ______.
Extra _______ slows, then stops the __________.
With greater _________ pressure than _______, the star _________ and _______, moving to the ___ on the ___ diagram.
A _______ temperature means that there is _____ radiation so the ___________ drops, leading to a drop in ____________.
A drop in ___________ means _____ radiation pressure
The cepheid variable cycle repeats itself.

Key points

Cepheids are used as '**standard candles'** for distance determination.

The period-luminosity law gives the luminosity from the period, and using brightness the distance can be found.

2.5 Stellar evolution on the HR diagram

Stellar processes and evolution

Formation of stars

The evolution of a star depends on its mass. The main stages are shown in the flow chart below. NOTE mass is given here in terms of the Solar mass ($1M_{\odot}$) and masses for the limits at each stage are after any mass loss.

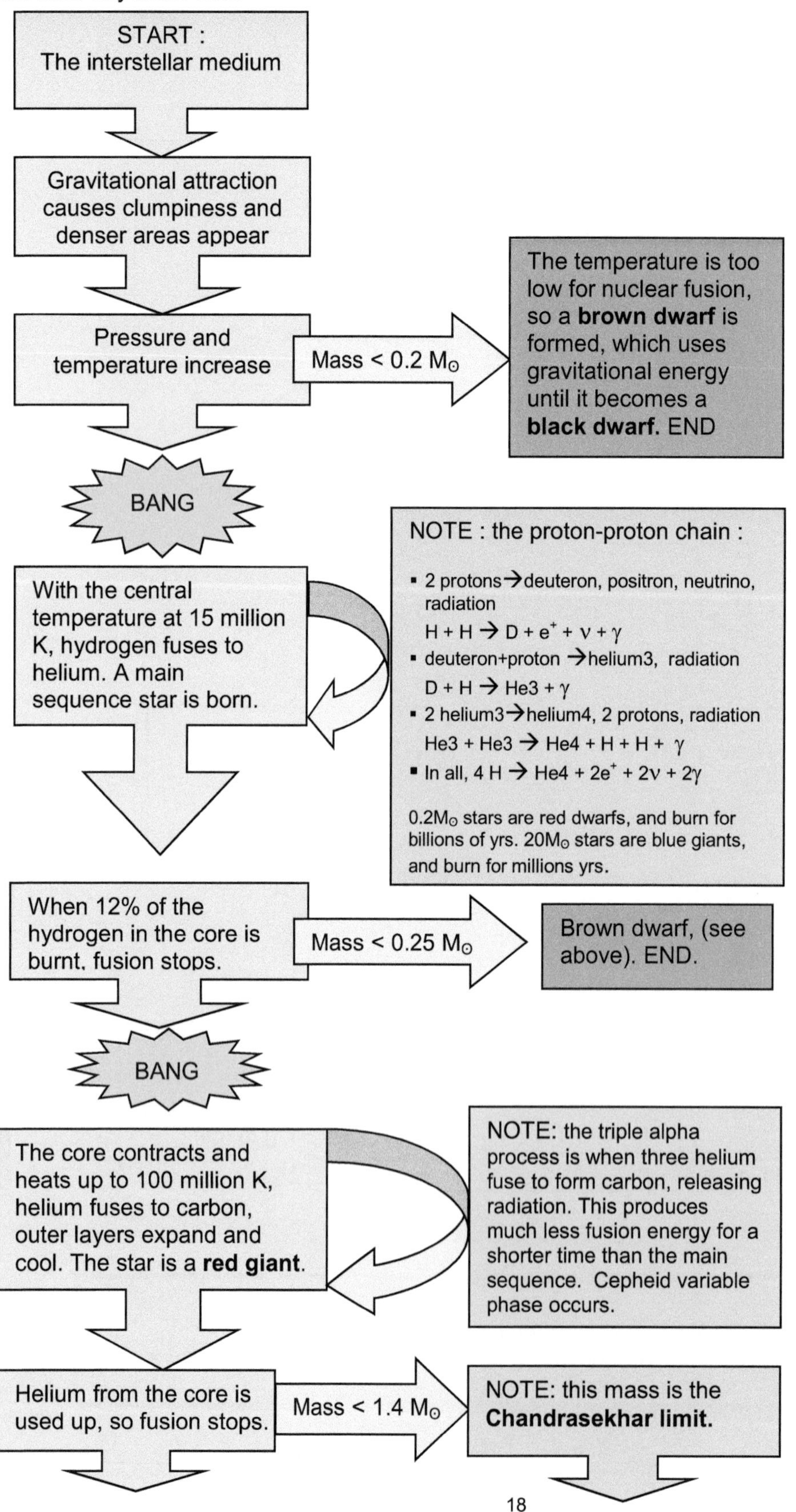

START :
The interstellar medium
Gravitational attraction causes clumpiness and denser areas appear
Pressure and temperature increase
Mass < 0.2 M⊙
The temperature is too low for nuclear fusion, so a **brown dwarf** is formed, which uses gravitational energy until it becomes a **black dwarf.** END
BANG
With the central temperature at 15 million K, hydrogen fuses to helium. A main sequence star is born.
NOTE : the proton-proton chain :
2 protons→deuteron, positron, neutrino, radiation
H + H → D + e⁺ + ν + γ
deuteron+proton →helium3, radiation
D + H → He3 + γ
2 helium3→helium4, 2 protons, radiation
He3 + He3 → He4 + H + H + γ
In all, 4 H → He4 + 2e⁺ + 2ν + 2γ
0.2M⊙ stars are red dwarfs, and burn for billions of yrs. 20M⊙ stars are blue giants, and burn for millions yrs.
When 12% of the hydrogen in the core is burnt, fusion stops.
Mass < 0.25 M⊙
Brown dwarf, (see above). END.
BANG
The core contracts and heats up to 100 million K, helium fuses to carbon, outer layers expand and cool. The star is a **red giant**.
NOTE: the triple alpha process is when three helium fuse to form carbon, releasing radiation. This produces much less fusion energy for a shorter time than the main sequence. Cepheid variable phase occurs.
Helium from the core is used up, so fusion stops.
Mass < 1.4 M⊙
NOTE: this mass is the **Chandrasekhar limit.**

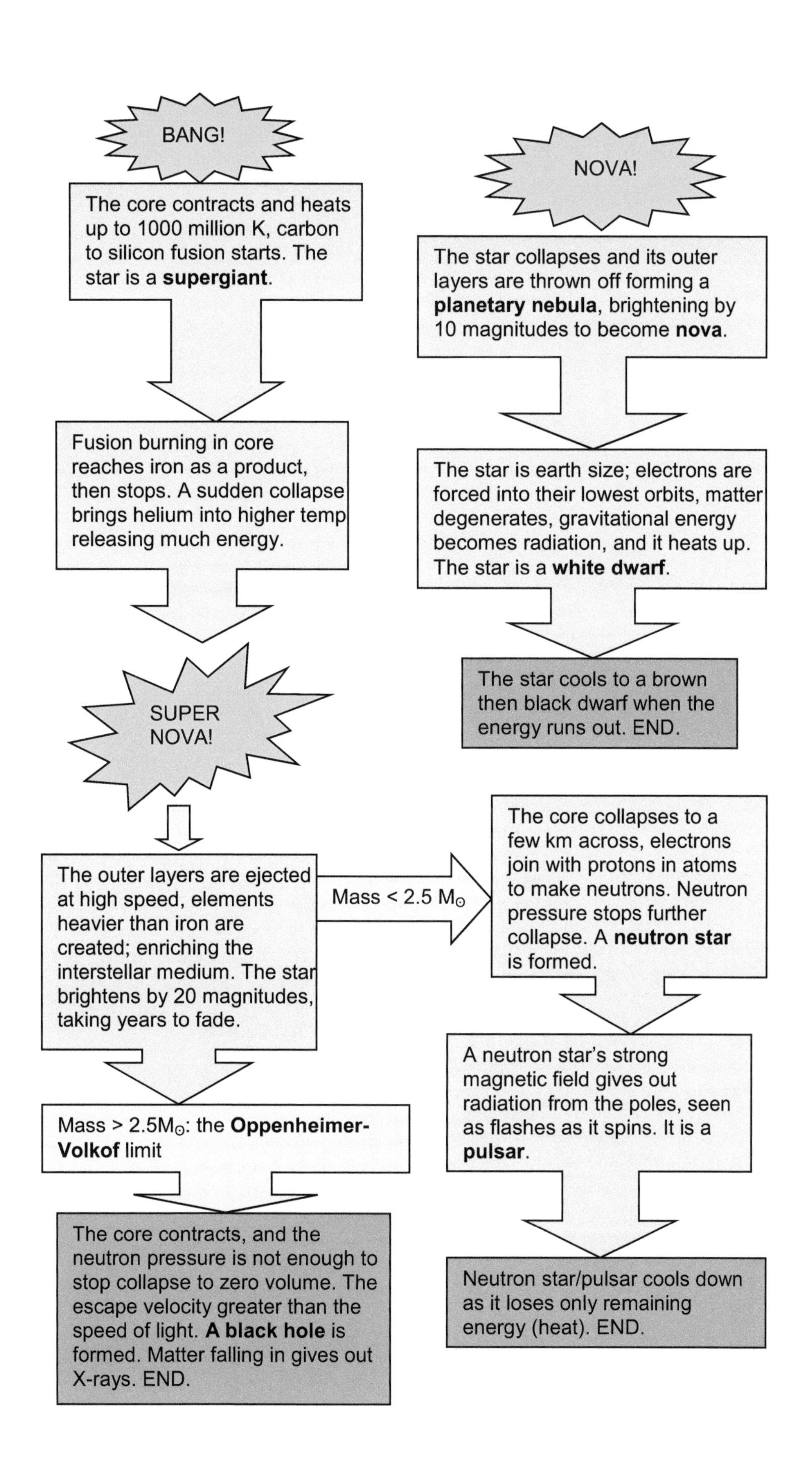
BANG!
The core contracts and heats up to 1000 million K, carbon to silicon fusion starts. The star is a **supergiant**.
Fusion burning in core reaches iron as a product, then stops. A sudden collapse brings helium into higher temp releasing much energy.
SUPER NOVA!
The outer layers are ejected at high speed, elements heavier than iron are created; enriching the interstellar medium. The star brightens by 20 magnitudes, taking years to fade.
Mass < 2.5 $M_{\odot}$
Mass > 2.5$M_{\odot}$: the **Oppenheimer-Volkof** limit
The core contracts, and the neutron pressure is not enough to stop collapse to zero volume. The escape velocity greater than the speed of light. **A black hole** is formed. Matter falling in gives out X-rays. END.
NOVA!
The star collapses and its outer layers are thrown off forming a **planetary nebula**, brightening by 10 magnitudes to become **nova**.
The star is earth size; electrons are forced into their lowest orbits, matter degenerates, gravitational energy becomes radiation, and it heats up. The star is a **white dwarf**.
The star cools to a brown then black dwarf when the energy runs out. END.
The core collapses to a few km across, electrons join with protons in atoms to make neutrons. Neutron pressure stops further collapse. A **neutron star** is formed.
A neutron star's strong magnetic field gives out radiation from the poles, seen as flashes as it spins. It is a **pulsar**.
Neutron star/pulsar cools down as it loses only remaining energy (heat). END.

Activity: the stellar evolution flow chart has been drawn again, with keys words removed. Fill in the blank spaces, then check back with the original. Good luck!

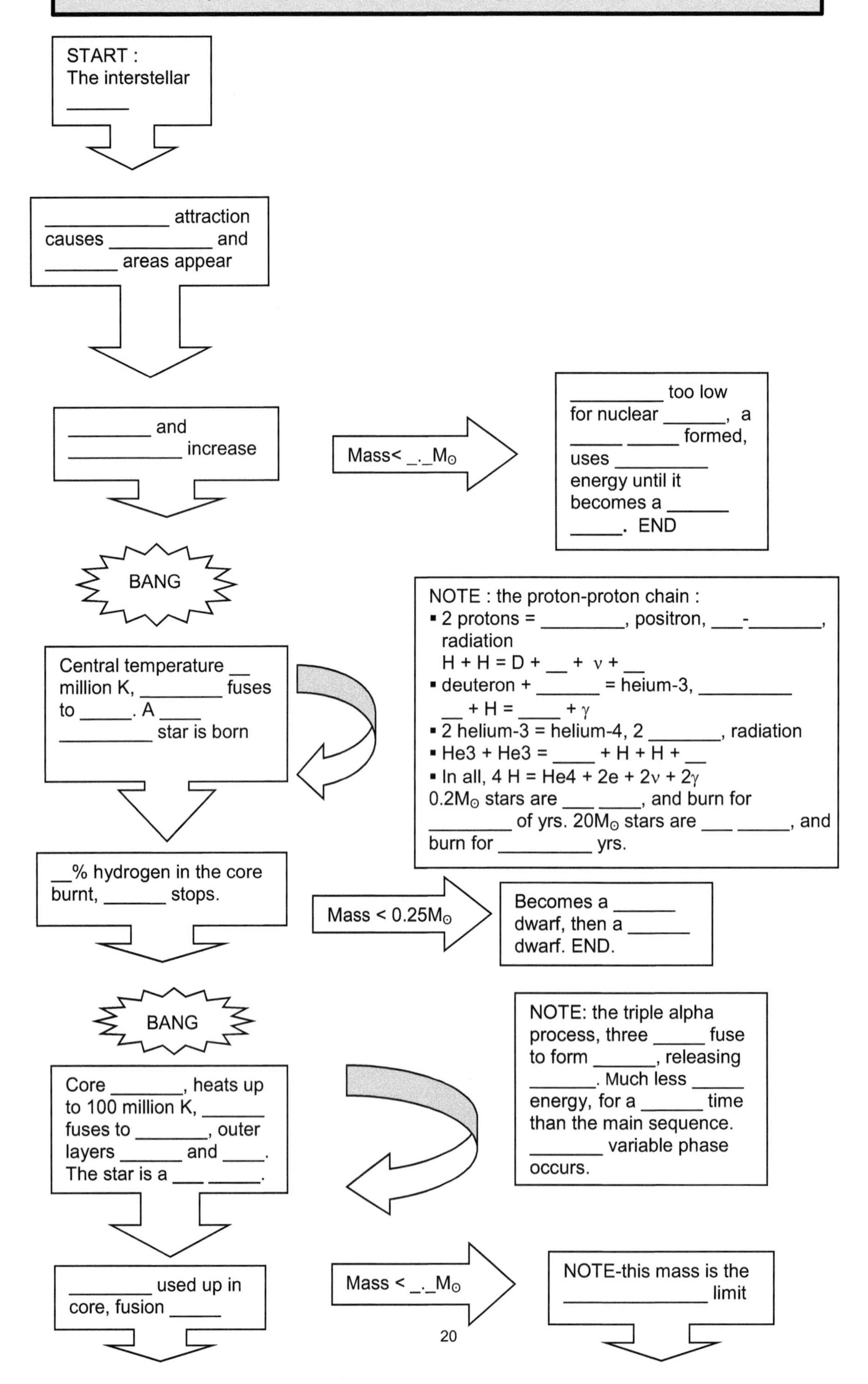

START :
The interstellar _______
____________ attraction causes ___________ and ________ areas appear
_________ and ____________ increase
BANG
Mass< _._$M_\odot$
__________ too low for nuclear _______, a _____ ______ formed, uses __________ energy until it becomes a ______ ______. END
Central temperature __ million K, _________ fuses to ______. A _____ __________ star is born
NOTE : the proton-proton chain :
▪ 2 protons = _________, positron, ____-________, radiation
H + H = D + __ + ν + __
▪ deuteron + _______ = heium-3, __________
__ + H = _____ + γ
▪ 2 helium-3 = helium-4, 2 ________, radiation
▪ He3 + He3 = _____ + H + H + __
▪ In all, 4 H = He4 + 2e + 2ν + 2γ
0.2$M_\odot$ stars are ____ _____, and burn for _________ of yrs. 20$M_\odot$ stars are ____ ______, and burn for __________ yrs.
__% hydrogen in the core burnt, _______ stops.
Mass < 0.25$M_\odot$
Becomes a _______ dwarf, then a _______ dwarf. END
BANG
Core ________, heats up to 100 million K, _______ fuses to ________, outer layers _______ and _____. The star is a ____ ______.
NOTE: the triple alpha process, three ______ fuse to form _______, releasing ________. Much less ______ energy, for a _______ time than the main sequence. ________ variable phase occurs.
_________ used up in core, fusion ______
Mass < _._$M_\odot$
NOTE-this mass is the _______________ limit

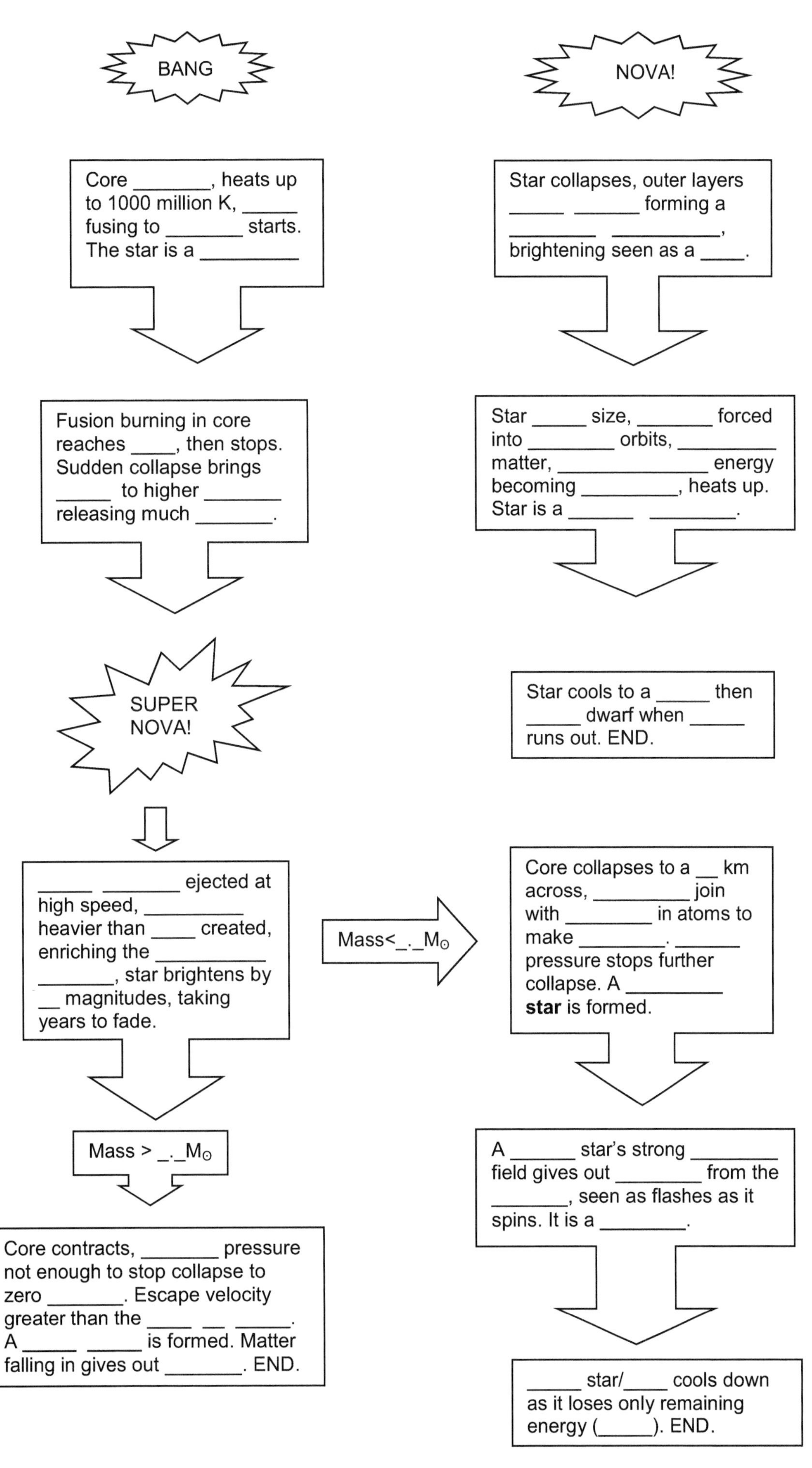

BANG
Core ________, heats up to 1000 million K, ______ fusing to ________ starts. The star is a __________
Fusion burning in core reaches _____, then stops. Sudden collapse brings ______ to higher ________ releasing much ________.
SUPER NOVA!
______ ________ ejected at high speed, __________ heavier than _____ created, enriching the ___________ ________, star brightens by __ magnitudes, taking years to fade.
Mass > _._M⊙
Core contracts, ________ pressure not enough to stop collapse to zero ________. Escape velocity greater than the _____ __ ______. A ______ ______ is formed. Matter falling in gives out ________. END.
Mass<_._M⊙
NOVA!
Star collapses, outer layers _____ ______ forming a _________ __________, brightening seen as a _____.
Star _____ size, ________ forced into _________ orbits, __________ matter, _______________ energy becoming _________, heats up. Star is a ______ _________.
Star cools to a _____ then _____ dwarf when _____ runs out. END.
Core collapses to a __ km across, _________ join with _________ in atoms to make _________. ______ pressure stops further collapse. A _________ **star** is formed.
A _______ star's strong _________ field gives out _________ from the ________, seen as flashes as it spins. It is a _________.
_____ star/_____ cools down as it loses only remaining energy (______). END.

Task 11: where does helium to carbon fusion start?
A 10^6K B 10^7K C 10^8K
D 10^9K.

Key points
Solar mass stars become red giants then white dwarfs.
Stars ending with 1.4-2.5$M_{\odot}$ become neutron stars.
Stars ending with >2.5$M_{\odot}$ become black holes.

D2.6 Types of stars

Red giants

- A star like the sun becomes a red giant when all its hydrogen has undergone fusion.
- Its core contracts and heats up until helium to carbon fusion starts.
- Its outer layers expand and cool, hence the name red giant.

White dwarf

- When a star like the sun has completed its fusion, there is no radiation to stop gravity.
- The star contracts so much, it pushes electrons into the lowest shells.
- This electron pressure stops further collapse and balances gravity.
- This process is called **electron degeneracy** and the star is called a **white dwarf**.
- A white dwarf is planetary in size and has a mass up to 1.4 $M_{\odot}$ solar masses.
- This mass is known as the **Chandrsaker Limit**.

Pulsars

- A pulsar is a very fast spinning neutron star.

Neutron star

- A star between 1.4 and 2.5 $M_{\odot}$ solar masses evolves into a neutron star.
- After the supernova explosion all the electrons are pushed into the nuclei.
- This turns all the protons into neutrons.
- It is the neutron pressure that stops further collapse and balances gravity.
- This is known as **neutron degeneracy**.
- The density of a neutron star is a thousand billion times that of water.
- It is only a few km across!
- The 2.5 $M_{\odot}$ solar mass limit is known as the **Oppenhemer-Volkoff limit**.
- Consider a neutron star of 2$M_{\odot}$ and radius 5km:
  - the density can be found from density = mass/volume.
  - mass = 2 x 2 x10^{30} = 4 x 10^{30}kg and radius = 8km = 8000m
  - density = mass / volume = $M/\frac{4}{3}\pi r^3$
  - putting in the values one gets a density of 1.9 x 10^{18}kgm^{-3}.
- Now consider a neutron of mass 1.7 x 10^{-27}kg and radius 10^{-15}m. Its density can be found in the same way. Calculate it:
  - you get 1.3 x 10^{18} kgm^{-3}. A neutron star has a similar density! Surprise!
- Due to conservation of angular momentum, as a star shrinks in size, it spins faster (think of the spinning ice skater pulling in her arms).
- A neutron star could be taking only milliseconds to rotate once on its axis.
- Neutron stars have very strong magnetic fields, whose poles don't quite match up with their geographic poles.
- Charged particles falling into their fields at the poles release radiation.
- The aurora borealis or northern lights on the earth form in a similar way.
- These flashes are seen every time the neutron star spins if we are in the path of the beam (much like the beam of light from a lighthouse).
- A neutron star that is seen to flash is called a **pulsar**. Such a star has been detected in the Crab Nebula, and is the remains of a supernova explosion seen in 1054.

Task 12: the fastest spinning pulsar has a radius of 5km and a frequency of 667Hz. Find the speed of the surface and compare it to that of light. What is the centripetal acceleration on the surface of the pulsar? If it has a mass 2$M_{\odot}$ then what is the acceleration due to gravity on the surface?

Key points
White dwarfs balance weight with electron degeneracy pressure.
Neutron stars balances weight with neutron degeneracy pressure.
A black hole's escape velocity is greater than the speed of light.

D2.7 The role of mass in evolution

If the mass of a remaining star after the supernova phase exceeds 2.5 $M_\odot$ solar masses, then the neutron pressure is not enough to stop further collapse. The star will contract indefinitely until it occupies zero volume! At some point the escape velocity will exceed the speed of light.
Thus, any light trying to leave the stars surface cannot escape, hence the name black hole.
In reality, matter falling into a black hole gives out radiation in the form of X rays so they can be 'seen' by detecting this radiation.

Task 13: what is the density of a black hole?

Exam Question Box 2: time for a quick review. Fill in the missing key words in the spaces below, then check back. Good luck!

(1) spectrum: a spectrum from a pure element at low pressure. (2) spectrum: the spectrum of a star. (3) diagram: a graph of the luminosity of a star against its surface temperature. (4) the colour of the hottest stars. (5) the colour of the coolest stars. (6) stars that are burning hydrogen by fusion. (7) stars that are burning helium, and have expanded and cooled. (8) a star the size of the earth with no more fusion energy. (9) stars that are burning carbon and are large and luminous. Main Sequence stars follow a (10) law. Stars that vary in brightness over a few days due to variation in size are (11) variables. When they increase in size the temperature goes (12). The period of these variables depends on (13) and as they are used to determine distance they are called (14). Stars that cannot start fusion are (15) dwarfs. Below the (16) limit stars become white dwarfs. Stars above the (17) limit become black holes, while those in between become (18) stars. The end result for a star depends on its (19). The outer layers blown off a giant going nova is called a (20).

1.	2.	3.	4.	5.	6.	7.	8.	9.
10.	11.	12.	13.	14.	15.	16.	17.	18.
19.	20.							

Key points
A star with a final mass below 1.4$M_\odot$ becomes a white dwarf
Between 1.4 and 2.5$M_\odot$ the star becomes a neutron star
Above 2.5$M_\odot$ the star becomes a black hole

D2 Answers

Task 7: Diffraction grating
Task 9: 23 000
Task 10: 4 000L, 530ly 160pc
Task 11: C
Task 12: About 21 000kms^{-1} or 7% that of light! 8.8 x $10^{10}ms^{-2}$., 1.1 x $10^{13}ms^{-2}$.
Task 13: Infinite!
Exam Question 2 Answers:

1. line emission	2. absorption	3. Hertzsprung Russell
4. blue	5. red	6. main sequence
7. red giants	8. white dwarf	9. supergiants
10. mass luminosity	11. cepheid	12. down
13. luminosity	14. standard candles	15. brown
16. Chandrasaker	17. Oppenhemer Volkoff	18. neutron
19. mass	20. planetary nebula	

D3 Cosmology

D3.1 The Big Bang model, space + time

Olber's Paradox and the Big Bang Model

- Newton thought that the universe was infinite and static.
- BUT if the universe was infinite, then in whichever direction we looked, we should see stars.
- If there was a star in every direction, then the night sky should look uniformly bright, the same brightness as the surface of the stars!
- However the night sky is black, so this model of the universe must be wrong. This is known as **Olber's Paradox**.
- NOTE that the derivation showing the paradox is no longer on the program.
- Newton's law of gravity states that every piece of matter pulls on every other piece of matter.
- Objects are either moving closer together due to gravity, or moving fast enough apart to escape the pull of gravity.
- The universe cannot be static - it must be finite and in motion.
- the Big Bang can help resolve this paradox:
  - Firstly, if the universe is finite, then there will not be an infinite number of stars, so the night sky will not be infinitely bright.
  - Secondly, the universe is expanding, so the light from the stars is red shifted to lower energies, reducing the brightness further.
  - Finally, the light from stars too far away has not yet reached us.

Task 14: what would be the implication if the light from all the other galaxies was blue shifted?

Key points
The universe is finite but unbounded.
The universe is expanding.

D3.2 Cosmic microwave radiation

Background radiation

- The temperature of a black body can be found from the peak in the curve as shown earlier using Wien's law.
- Penzias and Wilson found black body radiation coming from the universe.
- The **background radiation** peak is in the microwave part of the spectrum.
- The radiation is the same strength in all directions (isotropic).
- Wein's law indicates that it has a temperature of about 3K.
- The universe itself is behaving like a black body at 3K.
- As it is expanding, it is also cooling so obeying the Gas Laws.
- For example, in a diesel engine the gas is compressed suddenly in the cylinder so heats up enough to ignite the fuel.
- Another example is in a CO_2 cylinder when the gas is allowed to rapidly escape and expand, so it cools down enough to become dry ice at -78°C.
- In the past, the universe was at a much higher temperature.

Task 15: find the wavelength at peak intensity for the background radiation.

Key points
Penzias and Wilson first found the cosmic microwave background radiation.
It is from a black body of a temperature 3K.
This suggests the universe is cooling down from a very hot explosion.

D3.3 Hubble's Law, H, z and R

Red Shift - The Doppler Effect

- When there is relative motion between a source of waves and an observer the frequency changes. This is called the **Doppler Effect**.
- If a star moves away from us, the wavefronts are created further apart compared to the star at rest.
- The wavelength is longer so the frequency is lower.
- This lower frequency means that the light is shifted to the red end of the spectrum - a **red shift**.
- If a star is approaching us, the wavefronts are created closer together, compared to the star at rest.
- The wavelength is shorter so the frequency is higher.
- This higher frequency means that the light is shifted to the blue end of the spectrum - a **blue shift**.
- This allows us to study the rotation of a star or galaxy; one side will be approaching us (light is blue shifted) and the other side is moving away from us (red shifted).
- Galaxies in our Local Group show a mixture of blue and red shifts.
- This is because they are bound by gravity and on average some will be orbiting towards us and some orbiting away from us.
- Outside the Local group, all other galaxies show a red shift. This means they are all moving away from us.
- The fainter ones (and therefore more distant) are moving away faster.
- If all galaxies are moving away from us, the further ones more rapidly, this suggests that the universe is expanding.
- If the universe is expanding, then at some time in the past, it occupied a much smaller volume, following with an event like an explosion.
- This explosive start to the universe is called the **Big Bang** model.
- NB the Doppler Effect does not explain the Hubble expansion. *See below*.

Red shift of galaxies

- When light sources are moving away from us, the light is shifted to the red end of the spectrum. This example of the Doppler Effect is called the red shift. -Light sources approaching us show a blue shift.
- The shifting of light to the blue end or the red end of the spectrum is seen with galaxies, both in connection with their rotation rates and their velocities towards or away from us.

Red shift equation

- Hydrogen is found everywhere in the universe.
- The wavelengths of the lines in the hydrogen spectrum are known.
- So changes in their positions can be easily detected.
- The positions of the lines in a spectrum can be measured and then compared to the known wavelengths.
- If the lines show a blue shift, the object is approaching us.
- If they show a red shift then the object is moving away.
- If the velocity of the light source is v and the speed of light is c, the original wavelength is λ and the change in wavelength $\Delta\lambda$ then they are related:

Velocity of source ÷ velocity of light = wavelength change ÷ wavelength

$$\frac{v}{c} = \frac{\Delta\lambda}{\lambda}$$

Worked example:
If the hydrogen line of 650nm in the lab is found to be 683nm from a particular galaxy, the galaxy is moving away from us at: v÷c = (683-650)÷650 (speed of light being 300 000kms^{-1})
v = 15 000kms^{-1}

Task 16: if the hydrogen line above was shifted to 637nm, find the velocity.

Note that this equation applies to velocities well below the speed of light and therefore ignores relativity.

Hubble's Law

- If galaxies are a similar type, fainter ones are further away.
- Hubble measured the Doppler Shift in galactic spectra.
- Hubble noticed that the fainter (distant) galaxies had a greater red shift than the brighter (nearby) galaxies, so are moving away from us at a faster rate.
- Hubble found a linear relationship between the recessional velocity of a galaxy and its distance. This is known as **Hubble's Law**.
- The Milky Way belongs to the Local Group of galaxies.
- These two dozen galaxies orbit about their common centre of gravity.
- Half show a blue shift, half show a red shift, due to their random motions.
- Outside the Local Group, every cluster of galaxies shows a red shift.
- All galactic clusters are moving away from us.

If v is the recessional velocity in kms^{-1} and d is the distance in megaparsecs Mpc, then Hubble's law states:

$$v = Hd$$

Where H is the **Hubble constant**.

Graph of Hubble's Law

Practise Question: a galaxy that is moving $200kms^{-1}$ away from us is 4Mpc away. Take this information and plot it onto the graph shown below. Join this point to the origin with a straight line.

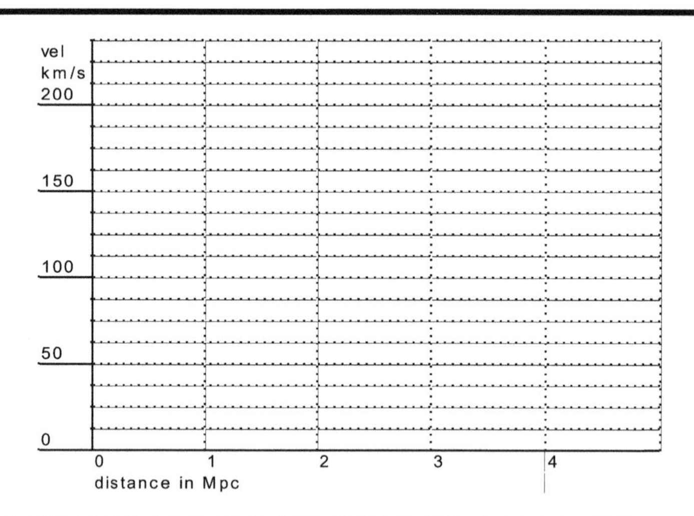

Task 17: a galaxy is 1.5Mpc away. What is its red shift velocity?

Worked example:
Suppose a galaxy has a recessional velocity of $125kms^{-1}$. The graph can be used to find out how far away it is.Draw a line from $125kms^{-1}$ across the graph to the line and continue it down to the distance axis. The distance given is 2.5Mpc.

- As v = Hd, the gradient gives you the Hubble constant.

Practise Question: measure the gradient of the graph. Don't forget units!

- The value of the Hubble constant is about H = 50 $kms^{-1}Mpc^{-1}$. This means that the recessional velocity of a galaxy increases by $50kms^{-1}$ for every Megaparsec it is away from us.

The age of the universe

- The more distant galaxies are moving faster away from us.
- Everything was once closer together, so the universe must be expanding.
- If the expansion rate is constant, one can find when the universe was created, as the distance between galaxies at that time would be zero.

Worked example:
Taking the Hubble constant to be $50kms^{-1}Mpc^{-1}$, how long would it take to travel 1Mpc at a speed of $50kms^{-1}$?
$50kms^{-1} = 5 \times 10^4 ms^{-1}$. This is the velocity v.
1Mpc is 3.26×10^6 light years (1pc = 3.26ly)
A light year is 9.5×10^{15}m, so 1Mpc is 3×10^{22} m. This is the distance x.
As velocity = distance/time, then time = distance/velocity, t = x/v
t = $3 \times 10^{22} / 5 \times 10^4$ which is 6×10^{17} sec, or about 20 billion years.

Task 18: if the oldest object so far seen (13 billion yrs) was created at the beginning of the universe, what would be Hubble's constant?

Space time expansion

- Time and space began with the universe in the Big Bang.
- Objects are getting further apart and space itself is expanding.
- There is nothing outside the universe as space only exists within it.
- The universe is not expanding into an empty space, there is nothing outside space (not even a void!).
- Time did not exist before the Big Bang.

Development of the universe

- Gravity is slowing down the expansion of the universe.
- So the slowing depends on the density of the universe.
- A high enough density and gravity could slow down the expansion and even reverse it. Such a universe is said to be **closed**.
- A low enough density and the universe would expand at a steady rate. Such a universe is said to be **open**.
- Just the right density (critical) would mean that the expansion rate would eventually be stopped. Such a universe is said to be **flat**.
- It appears that there is only a fraction of the mass needed to stop the expansion in the universe.
- There may still be mass that cannot be seen. **Brown dwarfs** are bodies not quite massive enough to start fusion and become stars.
- Objects that no longer burn nuclear fusion are known as **black dwarfs** and could be distributed across the galaxy.
- Brown and black dwarfs are called **MACHOS** (massive compact halo objects) and might account for the missing mass.
- Missing mass could be in particles thought to be massless. They are known as **WIMPS** (weakly interacting massive particles).
- The **neutrino** is such a particle once believed to be massless but recently found to have a very small mass (1/17 millionth the electron mass!).
- But this is far from being enough to close the universe!
- The density that will stop the expansion of the universe with its present volume is called the **critical density**.
- If the density is greater than this then it will slow down the expansion, stop, then collapse and therefore become a closed universe.
- If the density is below critical, the universe will expand forever and be open.
- If it has exactly the critical value, then the universe will be flat and the expansion will be stopped (though it will take forever!).
- It was thought that there is not enough mass to stop the expansion of the universe. However, recent observations show that the universe is expanding at an accelerating rate and this is caused by dark energy. *See section D5.*

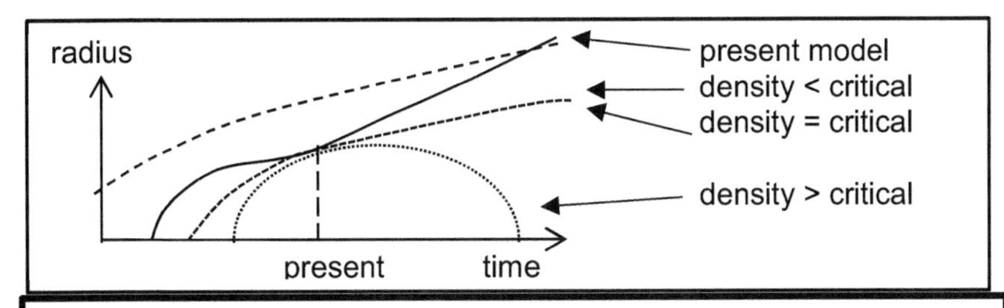

Key points
The recessional velocity of galaxies is proportional to their distance.
velocity = Hubble's constant x distance (v = Hd).
The age of the universe is found from the reciprocal of H.

D3.4 The accelerating universe and redshift z

- Consider the wavelength λ of a spectral line made in the lab.
- The same line is observed in a distance galaxy to be shifted to λ'.
- The change in wavelength $d\lambda$ is given by $\lambda' - \lambda$.
- A useful quantity is the ratio of change in wavelength to wavelength z:

so $z = (\lambda' - \lambda)/\lambda$ $\qquad$ $z = d\lambda/\lambda$

- If z is positive it means a redshift, if negative it shows a blue shift.
- For small changes in wavelength z approximates to the ratio of recessional velocity v of the galaxy to the velocity c of light:

$z = d\lambda/\lambda = v/c$

- This is used in Hubble's Law where the velocity is proportional to distance.
- it can also can be rearranged in the following way:

$z = \lambda'/\lambda - \lambda/\lambda = \lambda'/\lambda - 1$ or $\qquad 1 + z = \lambda'/\lambda$

- Supernovae type Ia are the end result of exploding white dwarf stars.
- They all have the same maximum luminosity L.
- When seen from earth they will have a brightness b.
- The distance to a type Ia supernova d can be found via:

$L = 4\pi r^2 b$

- Thus Ia supernovae can be used as standard candles.
- Not only this, the redshift in their spectra can be used to with Hubble's law to see how the expansion rate has changed since they exploded.
- By looking at a very distant type Ia supernova, it had been found that the expansion rate has increased and not slowed down as previously thought.
- The universe is expanding at an accelerating rate.

Key points
z is the ratio of wavelength change to wavelength.
The universe is expanding at an accelerating rate.

Task 19: a wavelength in the lab of 420nm measures 504nm from a galaxy. What is the z value?

D3.5 The Cosmic Scale factor R

- The **cosmic scale factor R** is the relative expansion rate of the universe.
- It is the ratio of the expansion rate at one time compared to a previous time.
- If the expansion rate was constant the cosmic scale factor would be 1.
- If the expansion was slowing down R would be less than one.
- If the expansion rate was increasing it would be greater than one.
- Present observations show that the scale factor is greater than one.
- This means that at present the universe is expanding at an accelerating rate.
- This rate seems to be becoming exponential with time.
- This can be explained by the presence of **dark energy** in the universe.
- The dark energy effectively causes repulsion and speeds up expansion.
- Thus dark energy makes the cosmic scale factor greater than one.

Key points
The cosmic scale factor R is the relative expansion rate of the universe. It is greater than one due to dark energy.

Exam Question Box 3: are you a Macho or a Wimp? Whatever you are, fill in the missing words in the spaces to the right then check the answers on the next page.

The idea that the universe started in a huge explosion is the (1) theory. CMB stands for (2). This peaks in the (3) part of the spectrum. (4) Effect is the apparent change in wavelength due to motion between source and observer. Hubble found that the (5) of galaxies was proportional to (6). The age of the universe is found from the reciprocal of (7). MACHO stands for (8). WIMP stands for (9). (10) density is the density that would stop the universe's expansion. The ratio of wavelength change to wavelength has the symbol (11). R is called the (12). It is the (13) of the universe. At present R is (14) than one. This is due to the presence of (15).

1.	2.	3.	4.	5.	6.	7.	8.	9.
10.	11.	12.	13.	14.	15.			

Task 20: suppose R started out at 0.98 then became 1.02, describe what happened to the universe.

D3 Answers

Task 14: The universe is contracting! The Big Crunch.
Task 15: About 0.97mm (Using T = 2.7K)
Task 16: -6000kms^{-1}, the negative sign showing the galaxy is approaching us.
Task 17: 75kms^{-1}
Task 18: 77Kms^{-1}Mpc^{-1}
Task 19: z = 0.2

Task 20: at first the rate of expansion was decreasing then the rate increased.

Exam Question 3:

1. Big Bang	2. Cosmic microwave background	3. Microwave	4. Doppler	5. Recessional velocitiy
6. Distance	7. H	8. Massive Compact Halo Objects	9. Weakly Interacting Massive Particles	10. critical
11. z	12. Cosmic scale factor	13. Relative expansion rate	14. Greater	15. dark energy

D4 Stellar processes

D4.1 Jeans criterion applied to star formation

- The interstellar medium is made up of gas and dust from supernovae.
- New stars form out of the interstellar medium.
- Gas cloud particles possess kinetic energy due to random thermal motion.
- The average kinetic energy is given by the temperature of the gas cloud.
- The force of gravity is balanced by the pressure exerted by the gas particles.
- However if they radiate some of the energy away, then gravity will exceed the pressure and the cloud will collapse.
- The particles in a gas cloud will also possess gravitational potential energy because they are all in the gravitational field of the cloud.
- **Jeans criterion** is the minimum mass of a gas cloud of given temperature, radius and density that will collapse under gravity to form a star.
- If M_j is the Jean mass and M the cloud mass then for the cloud to collapse

$M > M_j$

- If T is the temperature of the cloud and R the radius of the cloud, m_H the mass of a proton and μ the average atomic mass of atoms in the cloud then:

$$M_J = {}^{3kTR}/_{2\mu m_H}$$

- Where k is Boltzmann's constant and G the universal gravitational constant it is possible to find the radius of the cloud from which the sun formed:

let $\mu = 1.4$ so $m_H = 1.67 \times 10^{-27}$, $G = 6.67 \times 10^{-11}$, $k = 1.38 \times 10^{-23}$ and $M = 2 \times 10^{30}$kg and T = 10K

$$R = {}^{2G\mu m_h M_J}/_{3kT}$$

$$R = {}^{2 \times 6.67 \times 10^{-11} \times 1.4 \times 1.67 \times 10^{-27} \times 2 \times 10^{-30}}/_{3 \times 1.38 \times 10^{-23} \times 10}$$

$R = 1.5 \times 10^{15}$ m which is about 10000AU or 0.15ly

NOTE that this equation is not needed for the IB, nor given in the data book, but is included to illustrate how stellar formation uses Jean's Criterion.

Time on the main sequence

- The sun is halfway (4.7 billion years) through its life on the main sequence.
- It has therefore used up half its core hydrogen in fusion and is likely to spend some ten billion years on the main sequence.
- The lifetime of other main sequence stars can be calculated from this.
- From the mass-luminosity relation, L depends on $M^{3.5}$.
- Compare a star of mass M to the sun's mass $M_\odot$.
- A star of twice the mass of the sun would have twice the amount of fusionable hydrogen in its core.
- But such a star would burn at a greater rate $2^{3.5}$ ie about eleven times faster.
- As there is twice as much hydrogen it would last only $\frac{2}{11}$ times as long as the sun or about 1.8 billion years.

The general formula for a stars' lifetime on the main sequence would be:

time = (mass of sun ÷ mass of star)$^{2.5}$ x 10 billion years

$t = (M_\odot \div M)^{2.5} \times 10^{10}$ years

- as an example, take a star of ten solar masses. What is the MS lifetime?

$t = 0.1^{2.5} \times 10^{10}$ = 32 million years

Key points
Jean's criterion decides the minimum mass in a gas cloud for star formation.
A star's lifetime on the main sequence comes from the mass-luminosity law.

Task 21: what would be the life of a star of 0.5 solar masses?

D4.2 Nuclear fusion

The proton-proton chain

- When the core of a main sequence star like the sun has reached about 15 million K nucleosynthesis can take place.
- **Nucleosynthesis** is the creating of new nuclei from high energy collisions.
- In the sun's core helium is created via the proton-proton chain reaction.
- It starts with two protons colliding to make heavy hydrogen (a deuteron).
- In the reaction a positron, a neutrino and a gamma ray are also created.

2 protons → deuteron + positron + neutrino + radiation

$H + H \rightarrow D + e^{+} + \nu + \gamma$

- A third proton collides with the deuteron creating light helium and energy

deuteron + proton → helium3 + radiation

$D + H \rightarrow {}^{3}He + \gamma$

- Two light helium collide to make normal helium, two protons and energy

2 helium3 → helium4 + 2 protons + radiation

${}^{3}He + {}^{3}He \rightarrow {}^{4}He + H + H + \gamma$

- in all, four protons create helium, two positrons, neutrinos and gamma rays

$4\,H \rightarrow {}^{4}He + 2e^{+} + 2\,\nu + 2\gamma$

- The gamma rays created supply the radiation pressure to oppose gravity.
- The neutrinos do not interact with anything; they escape the sun and are detected on earth.
- These neutrinos are evidence that fusion is taking place in the sun.

The CNO cycle

- In more massive hotter stars, hydrogen to helium fuses via the CNO cycle:
  - A proton collides with carbon producing nitrogen-13.
  - The nitrogen-13 decays to carbon-13 by giving out a positron.
  - A proton collides with carbon-13 to make nitrogen-14.
  - Another proton collides with the nitrogen-14 to make oxygen-15.
  - Oxygen-15 decays to nitrogen-15 also giving out a positron.
  - Finally a proton collides with nitrogen-15 to create carbon-12 and helium.
  - In all, four protons have made helium while the carbon ends 'unchanged'.
  - Energy is released in the process in the form of gamma rays.

- The whole cycle is shown below:

$H + {}^{12}C \rightarrow {}^{13}N + \gamma$
${}^{13}N \rightarrow {}^{13}C + e^{+} + \nu$
$H + {}^{13}C \rightarrow {}^{14}N + \gamma$
$H + {}^{14}N \rightarrow {}^{15}O + \gamma$
${}^{15}O \rightarrow {}^{15}N + e^{+} + \nu$
$H + {}^{15}N \rightarrow {}^{12}C + {}^{4}He$

Key points
Main sequence stars turn hydrogen to helium via the proton proton chain.
Hotter, heavier stars turn hydrogen to helium via the CNO cycle.

Task 22: in the CNO cycle what other things have been created and how many are there of each?

D4.3 Nucleosynthesis off the main sequence

The triple alpha process

- When hydrogen fusion stops, radiation reduces, then gravity causes the star's core to contract.
- This contraction makes the core heat up to 100 million K, so helium fusion begins.
- Three helium nuclei collide to make carbon-12, releasing energy.
- Note: an alpha particle is a helium nuclei, hence the name of the process.

$^{4}He + {}^{4}He + {}^{4}He \rightarrow {}^{12}C + \gamma$

- The release of this radiation causes the outer layers of the star to expand.
- The expansion causes cooling so the surface is red.
- The star leaves the main sequence to become a red giant.
- Hydrogen burning continues outside the core where there is enough left.
- The triple alpha process releases much less energy than the proton-proton chain so this phase lasts for a much shorter time.

- When enough of the helium in the core becomes carbon this phase ends.
- The core contracts and helium burning continues in an outer shell.
- If the star is massive enough the temperature will rise to cause carbon fusion.
- Carbon fusion takes place in many ways; mainly two carbon fuse to become neon, which also releases energy and a helium nuclei.
- Another carbon fusion reaction creates oxygen.

- When enough of the carbon in the core becomes neon this phase ends.
- The core contracts and carbon burning continues in an outer shell.
- If the star is massive enough the temperature will rise to cause neon fusion.
- Neon fuses with helium to create magnesium.

- When enough neon becomes magnesium and oxygen this phase stops.
- The core contracts and neon fusion continues in an outer shell.
- If the star is massive enough the temperature will rise to cause oxygen fusion.
- Two oxygen nuclei fuse to create silicon.
- Each new stage releases less energy and lasts for less time.
- This process continues (if the star is heavy enough) until silicon fuses.
- Here two silicon form iron releasing the final source of fusion energy.
- Fusion of the previous elements continues in shells round the core.
- This process stops at iron.

Task 23: what burns in the shell between carbon and magnesium fusion?

Key point
The triple alpha process is the fusion of three helium nuclei to make carbon.

D4.4 The s and r processes for neutron capture

- Once the silicon is used up, radiation stops so gravity collapses the core.
- This is the start of a supernova explosion.
- During collapse, hydrogen and helium are brought to a higher temperature.
- Hydrogen (protons) combine with the electrons present to form neutrons.
- This is known as **inverse beta decay**.

$p + e^- \rightarrow n + \nu + \gamma$

- This creates a large number of neutrons during the supernova.
- These neutrons can be captured under slow or fast conditions.
- The **r-process** refers to **rapid neutron capture**.
- In order to create elements heavier than iron there has to be a series of neutrons captured one after another in a short period of time. This occurs in the collapsing core of supernovae.
- Such a process will continue until the half-life of the created nuclei is shorter than the times between neutron capture.
- As an example cadmium 110 can continue to capture five neutrons in a row until it becomes cadmium 115 which is unstable with a half-life of 2 days.
- Cadmium 115 decays by beta minus decay becoming indium 115.

$^{110}{}_{48}Cd + 5n \rightarrow {}^{115}{}_{48}Cd$
$^{115}{}_{48}Cd \rightarrow {}^{115}{}_{49}In + e^- + \overline{\nu}$

- The **s-process** refers to **slow neutron capture**.
- A nuclei that captures the neutron decays before the next capture.
- Thus it means slow in frequency of capture, not slow moving neutrons.
- The captured neutron becomes a proton, giving out a (minus) beta particle.
- As an example bismuth 209 captures a neutron to become bismuth 210.
- The bismuth 210 then decays, giving out an electron and anti-neutrino.
- It becomes lead 210.

$^{209}{}_{83}Bi + n \rightarrow {}^{210}{}_{83}Bi$
$^{210}{}_{83}Bi \rightarrow {}^{210}{}_{84}Pb + e^- + \overline{\nu}$

- The s-process occurs in stars in the Giant family.

Task 24: nucleus A captures several slow moving neutrons in a short time period. Nucleus B captures a few fast moving neutrons over a long time period. Which is the r and which is the s process?

Key points
The r process is fast neutron capture.
The s process is slow neutron capture.

D4.5 Type II and Ia supernovae

- A **type II supernova** is the result of a collapsing then exploding heavy star.
- The star's mass is between 8 and 40 solar masses.
- They occur in spiral but not elliptical galaxies.
- They have hydrogen emission lines in their spectra.
- After a star of this mass has reached iron and nickel in the fusion reaction, these elements can no longer release fusion energy. The radiation pressure is reduced and so no longer counteracts gravity.
- Below 1.4 solar masses electron pressure is enough to halt the collapse.
- However if the mass goes above this, the collapse is extremely rapid.
- The collapse can effectively push the electrons into the nucleus.
- This causes the protons to combine with electrons to form neutrons.
- This process is known as **inverse beta decay.**
- Neutron pressure can be enough to stop the collapse.

- The implosion is reversed a bit like a ball bouncing off a solid wall.
- The explosion can be at a high temperature and hence very fast.
- The material can exceed the escape velocity of the star.
- It is also during this stage that elements higher than iron/nickel are created in the nuclear collisions of the shock wave.
- Hence this is where heavier materials such as uranium are made.

- **Type Ia supernovae** occur in binaries where at least one is a white dwarf.
- The other star could be any star from a white dwarf to a red giant.
- If the white dwarf has enough carbon and oxygen and the temperature is high enough then it can still fuse them releasing energy.
- The temperature could rise high enough if the white dwarf mass was to rise.
- The mass can increase if it is drawn from the nearby binary companion as the gravitational pull of the oxygen/carbon rich white dwarf will pull material from the outer layers of its companion.
- This material will form an accretion disc round the white dwarf.
- As the material falls in, the white dwarf's mass increases.
- If the temperature rises enough its carbon can fuse with helium to form oxygen, as happens to stars already evolved away from the main sequence.
- Similarly the oxygen can also start fusing and though this may start slowly it becomes a runaway fusion reaction.
- This releases a large amount of energy in a matter of seconds.
- The suddenness causes matter to be accelerated to a high speed.
- It can also be triggered if two stars actually merge, though this is rare.
- A **light curve** is a graph of the brightness of a star as it changes with time.
- A type Ia supernova would have a light curve that rises very rapidly.
- It then reaches a maximum within days of the initial explosion.
- Brightness then falls approximately exponentially over the coming months.
- This rate of reduction is due to the unstable isotopes formed during the explosion such as nickel 56 which has a half-life of a few months.
- As this only happens to a narrow mass range of white dwarfs, the rise in luminosity is the same for all Ia supernovae.
- Hence they can be used as **standard candles**.
- Remember a standard candle is light source that can be used to measure distances, such as Cepheid variables.
- e.g., such a white dwarf may have a luminosity of 4×10^{22} W. When they go supernovae, the luminosity increases by a factor of about 5 billion, which can equal the luminosity of a whole galaxy for a short period!
- Suppose in a distance galaxy a type Ia supernova is seen that reaches a brightness of 1.4×10^{-13} Wm^{-2}. The distance to the supernova and hence galaxy can be found using

$$b = L/4\pi d^2$$

- making d the subject

$$d = \sqrt{L/4\pi b} = \sqrt{4\times10^{22}\times5\times10^{9}/4\times3.14\times1.4\times10^{-13}} = 1.07\times10^{22}\text{m}$$

$$d = \sqrt{L/4\pi b} = \sqrt{4\times10^{22}\times5\times10^{9}/4\times3.14\times1.4\times10^{-13}} = 1.07\times10^{22}\text{m}$$

- this is about a 1.13Mly or about 350kpc

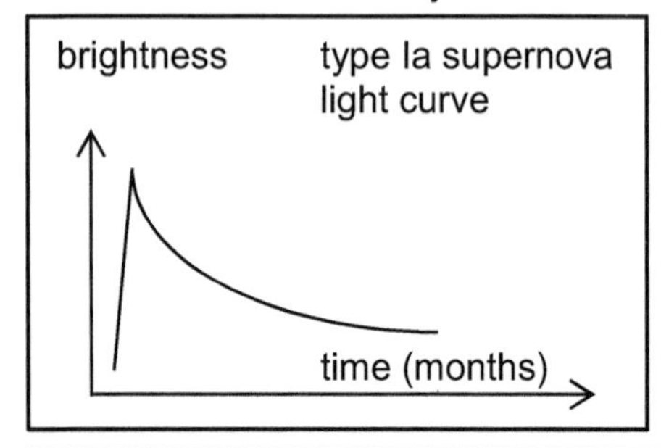

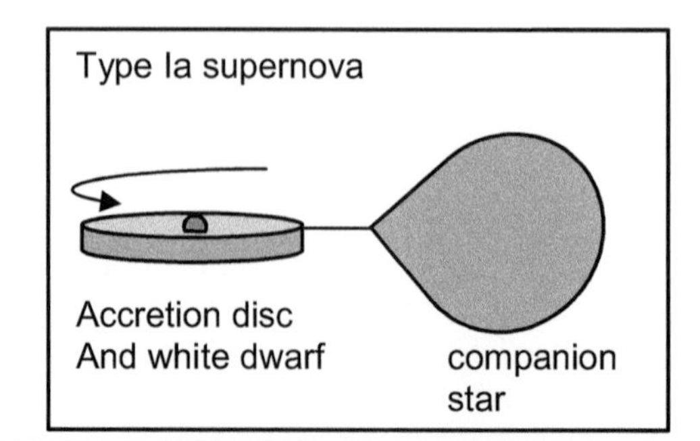

Task 25: if a similar white dwarf to the above goes supernova and is in the M51 galaxy which is 17 million ly distant, find its maximum brightness.

Key points
Type II supernovae form from collapsing exploding massive stars.
Type Ia supernovae form from white dwarfs in a binary system.

Exam Question Box 4: did you realise the carbon in your graphite pencil has come from a supernova?! Use it to fill in the missing words in the spaces on the right and marvel at this revelation! It's out of this world.

(1) Criteria is the minimum (2) of a gas cloud to form a star. The fusing of four hydrogen nuclei is the (3) chain. The (4) cycle involves the presence of carbon in forming helium. The (5) process is when three (6) nuclei form (7). Neon fuses with helium to form (8) the capture of an electron by a proton to form a neutron is called (9). The s process is (10) while the r process is (11). Type (12) supernovae are used as standard candles. Type (13) form from collapsing massive stars while type (14) form from white dwarfs in binary systems

1.	2.	3.	4.	5.	6.	7.
8.	9.	10.	11.	12.	13.	14.

D4 Answers

Task 21: about 57 billion yrs! 4 times the present age of the universe. $T=1/0.5^{2.5} \times 10^{10}$
Task 22: two positrons, two neutrinos and three gamma rays.
Task 23: neon.
Task 24: A is r | B is s.
Task 25: about 6×10^{-16} Wm^{-2}. $L=4 \times 10^{22}$ W x 5×10^{9} use $b = L/4\pi d^2$, put dist into m.

Exam Question 4:

1.Jean's	2.mass	3.proton proton	4.CNO	5.triple alpha	6.helium	7.carbon
8.magnesium	9.inverse beta decay	10.slow neutron capture	11.rapid neutron capture	12. Ia	13.II	14.aI

D5 Further Cosmology

D5.1 Cosmological principle

- The **cosmological principle**: the universe is **homogeneous** and **isotropic**
- This means that it is uniform and looks the same in all directions.
- Although the distribution of galaxies is clumpy, no part of the universe looks very different to any other.
- Imagine standing in the middle of a deep forest; trees may be scattered randomly, but a forest looks similar in all directions. If one walks to a different part of the forest, it would look much the same.
- Evidence suggests that seen from the earth, the universe is homogeneous.
- It is assumed the universe would look the same from any another place.
- As we cannot travel to a distant place this cannot (yet!) be proved.
- Observing more distant objects also means looking back in time.
- As the universe has been expanding, there must be a difference with time.

Task 26: the opposite of isotropic is: unisotropic, anisotropic, anti-isotropic or non-isotropic?

Key points
The universe is homogeneous and isotropic.
It is the same in all directions.
This is the cosmological principal.

D5.2 Rotation curves of galaxies

- A **rotation curve** for a galaxy is a graph of the velocity against the distance from the centre of the galaxy (the radial distance).
- Below is the Milky Way's rotation curve which is typical for a spiral galaxy:

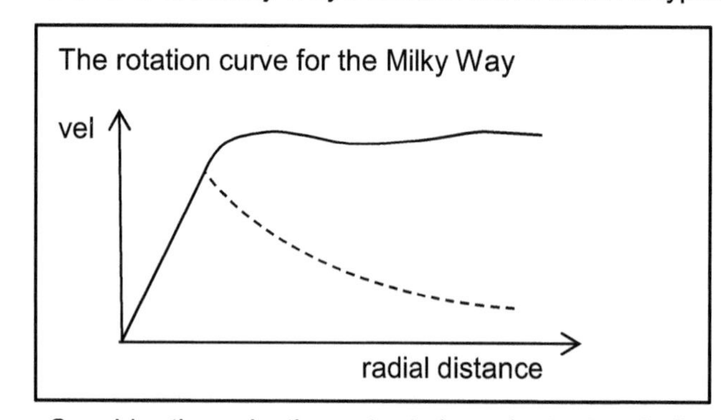

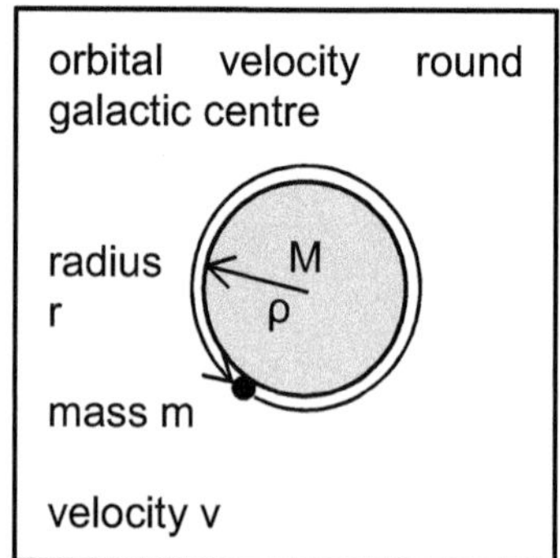

- Consider the galactic centre to be spherical and of a uniform density ρ.
- Consider a small mass m orbiting the centre at a distance r, velocity v.
- the centripetal force F is given by

$$F = mv^2/r$$

- This is due to the attraction from all the mass M within this radius.
- The mass m is only affected by the mass M within this radius.

The gravitational force F from M on the small mass m at distance r is:

$$F = GMm/r^2$$

as density = mass ÷ volume, this can be written mass = density x volume

$$M = \rho V$$

being a sphere of radius r, the volume V is given by:

$$V = {}^4/_3 \pi r^3$$

So:

$M = \rho \, {}^4/_3 \, \pi \, r^3$

substituting into the centripetal formula:

$F = G\rho \, {}^4/_3 \pi r^3 m \, / \, r^2$

$mv^2 / r = G\rho \, {}^4/_3 \pi r^3 m \, / \, r^2$

$v^2 = {}^4/_3 G\rho\pi r^2$

so:

$$v = \sqrt{\tfrac{4}{3}G\rho\pi} \times r$$

So, near the galactic centre, the velocity is proportional to distance.
This is shown by the straight line on the graph with the positive gradient.

$v \propto r$

As an example the sun is 8.3kpc from the galactic centre. If the density of the galactic centre is 1.2 x 10^{-21} kgm^{-3} and G is 6.67 x 10^{-11} $Nm^2\ kg^{-2}$ then first convert the distance to metres via 1pc = 3.26ly and 1 light yr is 9.46 x 10^{15} m

$r = 8300 \times 3.26 \times 9.46 \times 10^{15} = 2.56 \times 10^{20}$ m

so :

$$v = \sqrt{\tfrac{4}{3} \times 6.67 \times 10^{-11} \times 1.2 \times 10^{-21} \times \pi} \times 2.56 \times 10^{20} = 150\ 000ms^{-1} = 150kms^{-1}$$

- Beyond a certain distance the velocity is approximately constant.
- Imagine the matter in a galaxy was orbiting a point mass M in the centre.
- The velocity v should decrease with the root of the radial distance r.

If the only mass M was in the galactic centre then a small mass m at a distance r would experience a gravitational force F given by:

$F = GMm / r^2$

the force of gravity supplies the centripetal force with a velocity v:

$F = mv^2 / r$

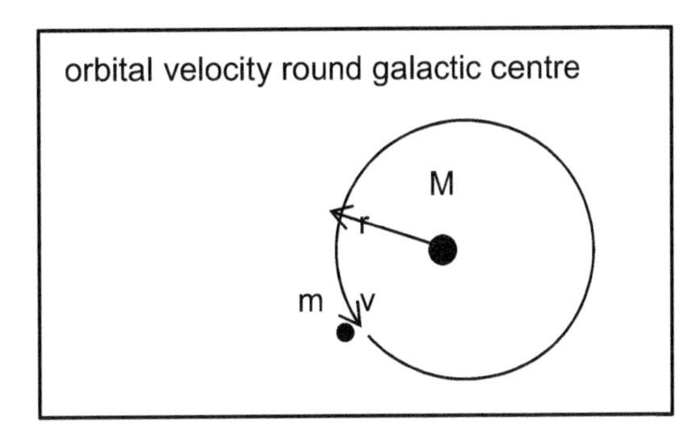

equating the two gives:

$Mv^2 / r = GMm / r^2$

cancelling out and making v the subject:

$$v = \sqrt{GM/r} \text{ so}$$

$v \propto 1/\sqrt{r}$.

- This is shown as the dotted line in the graph above.
- As the galaxy's mass is a disc, the rotation curve differs from this theory.
- There is a concentration of matter in the central bulge of a spiral galaxy.
- Mass in the centre will only be affected by the mass within its own radius.
- Inside a uniform sphere the gravitational force increases with radius.
- This makes the velocity increase with radius, as seen in the straight line.
- This accounts for the central portion rotating almost as a 'rigid body'.
- The outer section cannot be explained by the visible matter in the galaxy.
- The sun is 8.3kpc from the galactic centre and has a rotational velocity of $230kms^{-1}$. How long does it take to complete one orbit of the galaxy?

$v = 2\pi r \div T$ so $T = 2\pi r \div v = 2 \times 3.14 \times 2.65 \times 10^{20} \div 230\,000 = 7.0 \times 10^{15}$s

- This is about 220 million yrs and is known as a 'cosmic year'.

Task 27: Epsilon Aurige is 6.8kpc from the galactic centre. Find the velocity and its 'cosmic year' assuming a density 2.5×10^{-21}kgm^{-3}.

Key points
A rotation curve is a velocity radius graph for a galaxy.
The outer curve cannot be explained by the visible mass.

D5.3 Dark matter

- The galaxy's outer portion rotates as if there was more mass than is seen.
- The visible mass is seen by emitted, reflected or absorbed light.
- stars and emission nebulae give out their own light (see Orion's Nebula)
- Reflection nebulae are seen by the light they reflect from nearby stars.
- Absorption nebulae absorb light and hence look black (see the Coal Sac).
- **Dark matter** is inferred from its gravitational effect on the visible matter.
- It is invisible as it does not interact very much with radiation or visible matter.
- To account for the rotation curve of a galaxy the dark (and hence invisible) matter must occupy the spherical volume known as the Halo
- The visible matter is found in a disc shaped volume, thicker in the centre.
- There is about five times more dark matter than visible in the galaxy.

Task 28: the galaxy has a mass 4×10^{41}kg what will be the rotational velocity and period of a star on the edge of the galaxy a distance 25kpc from the centre (ignoring dark matter)? If one now includes the dark matter what would they be?

Key points
Dark matter is gravitationally attractive but gives out no radiation.
Its presence in the galaxy accounts for the faster outer rotation rate.

D5.4 Fluctuations in CMB radiation

- COBE, the Cosmic Background Explorer, is a satellite launched in 1989.
- It studied the background radiation from space in the infrared region.
- in 1992 it announced the discovery of anisotropies in the radiation:
- The universe behaves like a black body of temperature about 2.7K.
- Superimposed on this are temperature fluctuations of the order 10^{-4}K.
- This small variation is enough to explain the early formation of stars. The Inflationary Epoch is implied by gravity (symmetry) breaking from the other forces.
- It predicts that minor clumpiness of matter in the early universe is magnified by inflation allowing gravity to continue the clumpiness to form stars.

- WMAP stands for the Wilkinson Microwave Anisotropy Project.
- It is a satellite launched in 2001 to continue COBE's research.
- It improved the resolution on the cosmic background temperature.
- The results support the current Standard Model of Cosmology.
- It measured the Hubble constant and hence the age of the universe with a better than 1% precision.

- The Planck spacecraft was launched in 2009.
- Among the many aims of the mission was to study the anisotropy in the cosmic microwave background radiation, to a greater sensitivity and better angular resolution than WMAP.
- It confirmed the results of the previous studies.
- It made a full survey of the sky at a higher resolution and sensitivity.

- The results suggest a slightly older age for the universe.
- It is now thought to be nearly 13.8 billion years.
- The universe is 5% ordinary matter, 27% dark matter and 68% dark energy.
- The Hubble constant is measured at $68 kms^{-1}Mpc^{-1}$.

Task 29: what do COBE and WMAP stand for?

Key points
Hubble's constant is $68 kms^{-1}Mpc^{-1}$.
The universe is 13.8 billion yrs old.

D5.5 The Cosmological Redshift

- Redshift is the increase in wavelength from a light source.
- This can happen in three different ways:
  1. **Gravitational redshift** is an increase in wavelength due to light escaping from a strong gravitational field. This is covered in the relativity option.
  2. **The Doppler Effect** is the increase in wavelength from a light source that is moving away from the observer. This is what occurs for light from nearby galaxies.
  3. **Cosmological redshift** is the increase in wavelength from a distant galaxy due to the expansion of space.
- The best analogy is to imagine that space is a rubber sheet:
- When a distant galaxy gives out a photon of light, it has a certain wavelength. Imagine drawing that wave onto the rubber sheet.
- As space is expanding it is like stretching the rubber sheet. By stretching the sheet, the length of the wave increases.

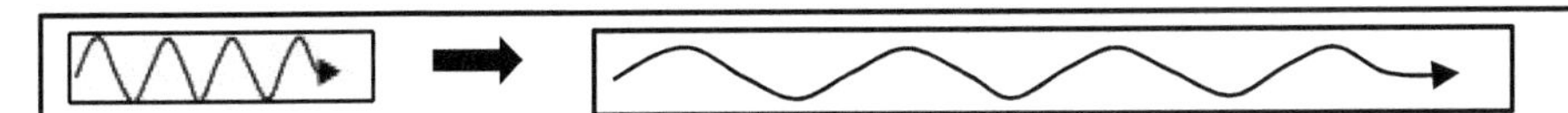

If space was like a rubber band, a photon's wavelength would increase as space stretches.

Task 30: measure the wavelength of both photons in the diagram above and find the ratio of final / initial wavelength.

Key points
The Doppler Effect explains the nearby redshift as due to relative velocity.
Cosmological redshift is caused by the expansion of space between galaxies.

D5.6 Critical density

- The **critical density** of the universe is the density that will slow down and eventually stop the expansion.
- Assuming the universe is homogeneous and isotropic, a spherical volume of radius r can be treated as if all its mass M in the centre (Newton's Laws).

mass escaping from a uniform density universe

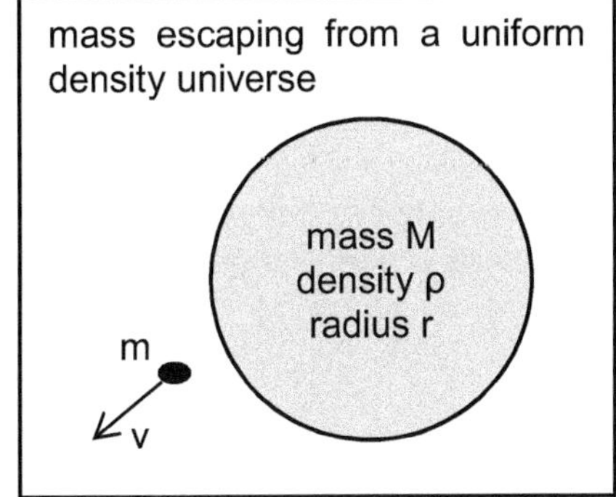

mass = density x volume
with ρ being density and V the volume:

$M = \rho V$

the volume V of a sphere radius r is:

$V = {}^4/_3 \pi r^3$
So $M = {}^4/_3 \rho \pi r^3$

- Consider a small mass m at the edge of the volume at the escape velocity v.
- This makes the density the critical density ρ_c as m can just escape.
- its gravitational potential energy E_p is given by:

$$E_p = -GMm/r$$

its kinetic energy E_k is:

$$E_k = ½\,mv^2$$

the velocity must be given by the Hubble equation:

$$v = Hr$$

Where H is the Hubble constant and r the distance (radius), so the kinetic energy lost equals the potential energy gained:

$$½m(Hr)^2 = GMm / r$$

m cancels out and M can be substituted with volume x density:

$$½H^2r^2 = {}^4/_3G\rho_c\pi r^3 / r$$

cancelling r and making the density the subject gives us:

$$\rho_c = 3H^2 / 8\pi G$$

- The Hubble constant units must be converted into SI units of sec^{-1} for the density to be in kgm^{-3}.

As an example take H = $77kms^{-1}Mpc^{-1}$ which is $77\,000ms^{-1}$ while 1Mpc must be converted into metres via 1pc = 3.26 ly and 1 ly = 9.46×10^{15}m

$$H = 77\,000 \div (10^6 \times 3.26 \times 9.46 \times 10^{15}) = 77\,000 \div 3.08 \times 10^{22} = 2.5 \times 10^{-18}s^{-1}$$

G is $6.67 \times 10^{-11}Nm^2kg^{-2}$ so the critical density is

$$\rho_c = 3 \times (2.5 \times 10^{-18})^2 \div 8\pi \times 6.67 \times 10^{-11} = 1.1 \times 10^{-26}\ kgm^{-3}$$

- This is the critical density of the universe - it's very small isn't it?!

Task 31: at what age of the universe would the critical density be exactly one hydrogen atom (proton) per cubic metre?

Key point
The critical density is that which will stop the expansion of the universe.

D5.7 Dark energy

- Observations from the 1990s showed that the rate of expansion of the universe was increasing.
- Until then it was thought that the expansion rate was slowing down.
- The slowing was considered to be due to the gravitational attraction of the mass of the universe.
- To explain the observations the concept of **dark energy** is theorised.
- Dark energy only interacts through the force of gravity.
- It is evenly but thinly spread throughout the universe.
- It exerts a negative pressure as if the force of gravity was repulsive.
- This repulsion would cause the expansion to accelerate.

Cosmic Scale Factor (CSF)

- The **cosmic scale factor** is the relative expansion rate of the universe.
- If the expansion rate was constant the cosmic scale factor would be 1.
- If the expansion was slowing down it would be less than one
- If the expansion rate was increasing it would be greater than one.
- Present observations show that the scale factor is greater than one.
- This means that at present the universe is expanding at an accelerating rate.
- This rate seems to be becoming exponential with time.
- This can be explained by the presence of dark energy in the universe.
- The dark energy effectively causes repulsion and speeds up expansion.
- Thus dark energy makes the cosmic scale factor greater than one.

- The temperature of the universe is inversely related to the radius.
- If the radius is increasing at a constant rate with time then the temperature is inversely related to time.

Task 32: what would a CSF of zero mean? What if it was -1?

Key points
Dark energy can explain the increasing expansion rate of the universe.
The cosmic scale factor is the relative expansion rate of the universe.
The temperature of the universe is inversely proportional to the radius.

Galaxies and the expanding universe

Galactic motion

- The galaxy in which the solar system is situated is called **the Milky Way**.
- The Milky Way is a member of the Local Group of galaxies.
- It is a spiral galaxy, with a central bulge of many closely packed stars, gas and dust, with a massive black hole in the centre.
- Outside the bulge is a flat disc of stars, dust and gas, in a spiral formation.
- The Milky Way is about 30kpc across, the sun 10kpc from the centre.
- It is enveloped in a spherical volume of material known as the **halo**. It is very tenuous, containing some very old stars, some peculiar stars with very eccentric orbits, and other matter (see earlier for missing mass).

Types of galaxies

- **Spiral galaxies** are disc shaped collections of stars, dust and gas. They have a central bulge, a tenuous halo and most of their material is in spiral arms.
- **Elliptical galaxies** are spheroidal collections of stars, dust and gas. These are more compact towards the centre, and range from perfectly spherical to very elliptical.
- **Irregular galaxies** which have no regular shape at all.

Galactic distribution

- A **galactic cluster** is a group of galaxies gravitationally bound together, orbiting around a common centre of gravity.
- Larger groupings of galactic clusters are called **superclusters**.
- The Local Group is a 'satellite' cluster of the large Virgo supercluster.

The Timeline of the Universe

The evolution of the universe is shown in the flow chart below

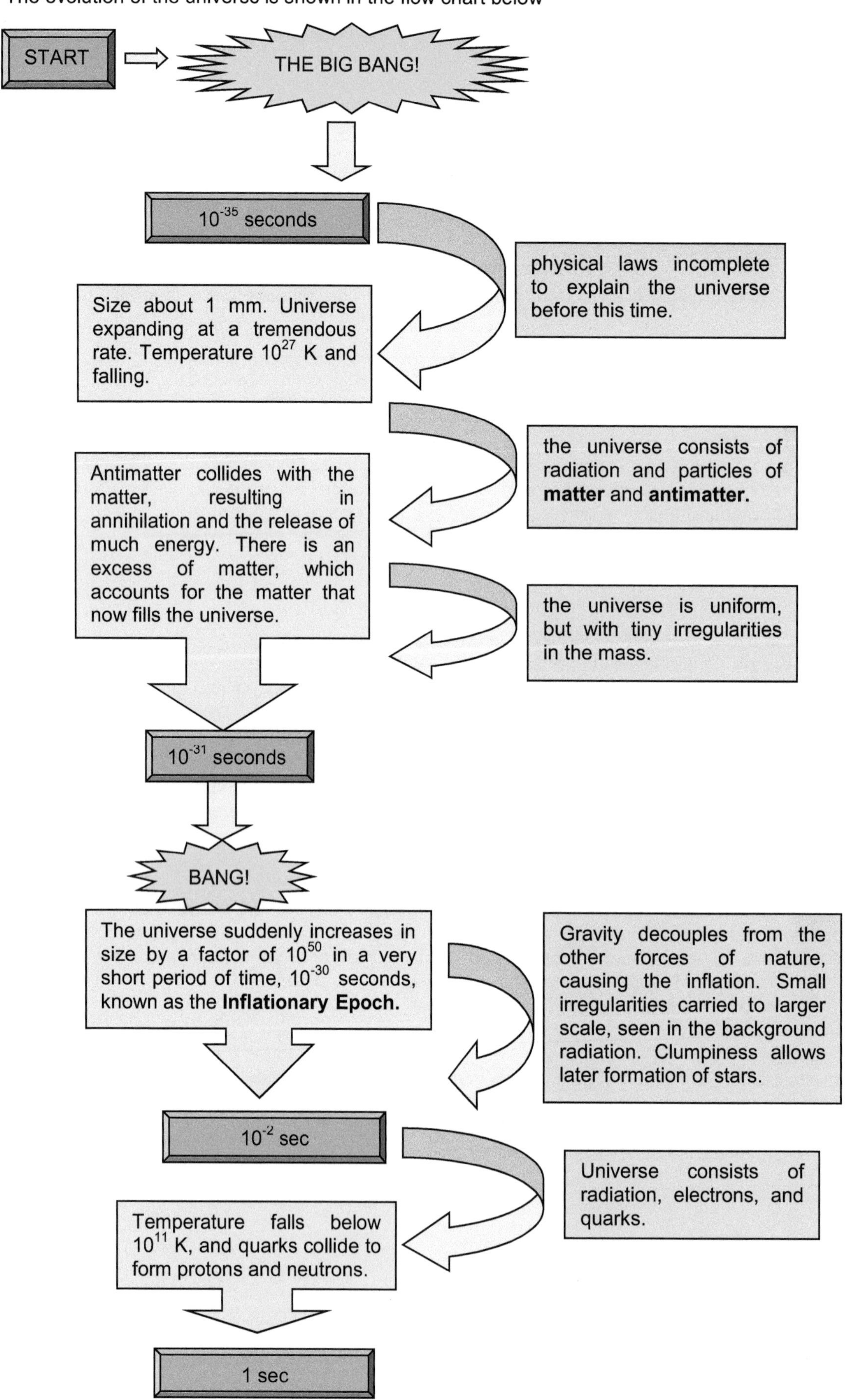

START
THE BIG BANG!
10^-35 seconds
physical laws incomplete to explain the universe before this time.
Size about 1 mm. Universe expanding at a tremendous rate. Temperature 10^27 K and falling.
the universe consists of radiation and particles of matter and antimatter.
Antimatter collides with the matter, resulting in annihilation and the release of much energy. There is an excess of matter, which accounts for the matter that now fills the universe.
the universe is uniform, but with tiny irregularities in the mass.
10^-31 seconds
BANG!
The universe suddenly increases in size by a factor of 10^50 in a very short period of time, 10^-30 seconds, known as the Inflationary Epoch.
Gravity decouples from the other forces of nature, causing the inflation. Small irregularities carried to larger scale, seen in the background radiation. Clumpiness allows later formation of stars.
10^-2 sec
Universe consists of radiation, electrons, and quarks.
Temperature falls below 10^11 K, and quarks collide to form protons and neutrons.
1 sec

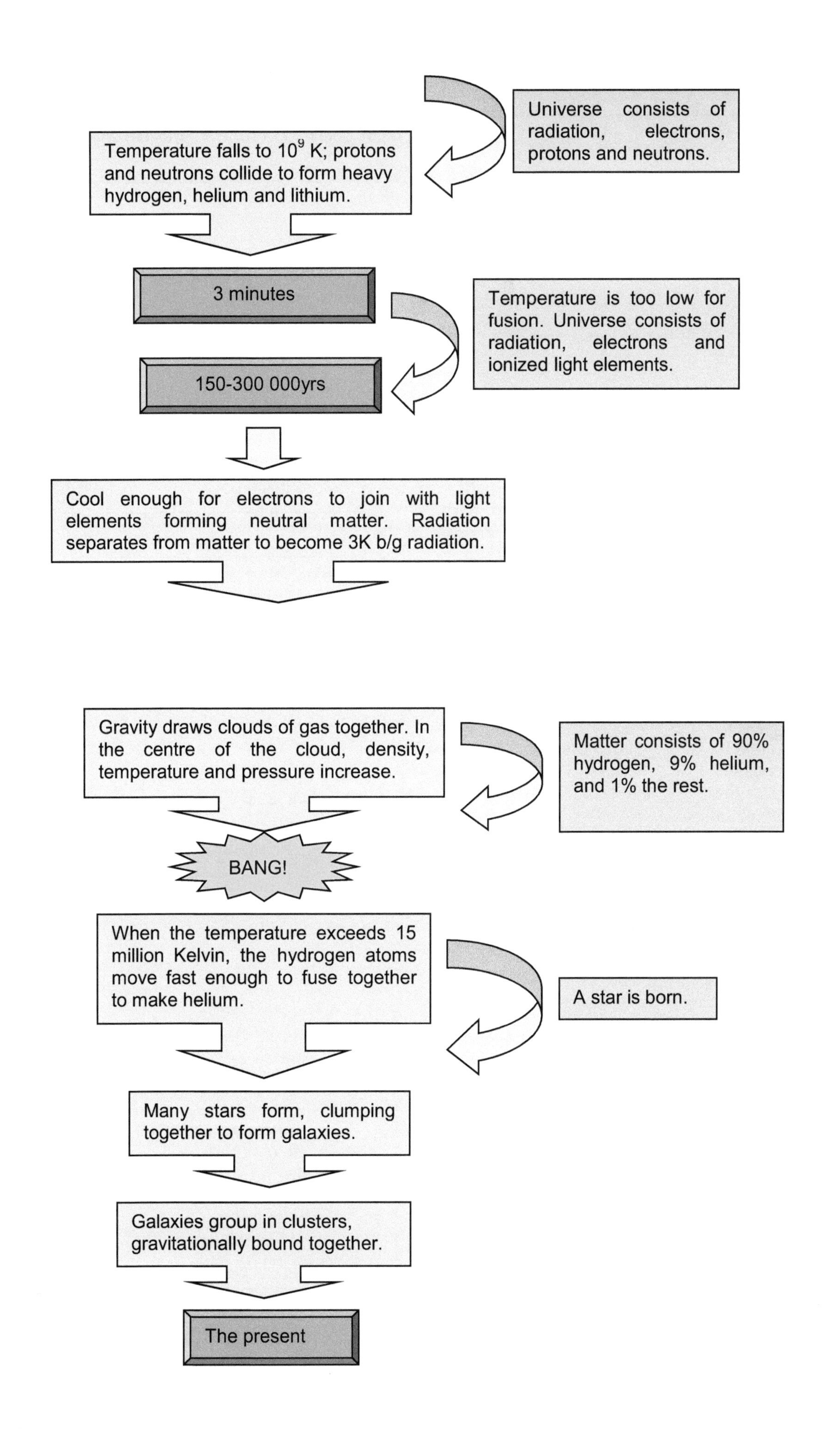
Universe consists of radiation, electrons, protons and neutrons.
Temperature falls to 10^9 K; protons and neutrons collide to form heavy hydrogen, helium and lithium.
3 minutes
Temperature is too low for fusion. Universe consists of radiation, electrons and ionized light elements.
150-300 000yrs
Cool enough for electrons to join with light elements forming neutral matter. Radiation separates from matter to become 3K b/g radiation.
Gravity draws clouds of gas together. In the centre of the cloud, density, temperature and pressure increase.
Matter consists of 90% hydrogen, 9% helium, and 1% the rest.
BANG!
When the temperature exceeds 15 million Kelvin, the hydrogen atoms move fast enough to fuse together to make helium.
A star is born.
Many stars form, clumping together to form galaxies.
Galaxies group in clusters, gravitationally bound together.
The present

Universe Timeline Revision

Practise Question: fill in the missing words in the flow chart below, then check your answers with the original. Good luck!

START

THE BIG BANG !

10^{-35} seconds

physical laws _________ to explain the universe before this time.

Size about 1 mm. Universe __________ at a tremendous rate. Temperature 10^{27} K and ________

the universe consists of ________ and particles of ________ and _________.

_________ collides with the ________, annihilating and releasing much _______, but there is an excess of _______, which accounts for the _____ that now fills the universe

the universe is _______, but with tiny __________ in the mass distribution.

10^{-31} seconds

BANG

the universe suddenly ____________ in size by a factor of 10^{50} in a very short period of time, 10^{-30} seconds, known as the __________ _________

________ decouples from the other forces of nature, causing the ________. Small irregularities carried to larger scale, seen in the _________ ________. Clumpiness allows later formation of _____.

10^{-2} sec

Universe consists of _______, ________, and ______.

Temperature falls below 10^{11} K, _____ collide to form ______ and _______.

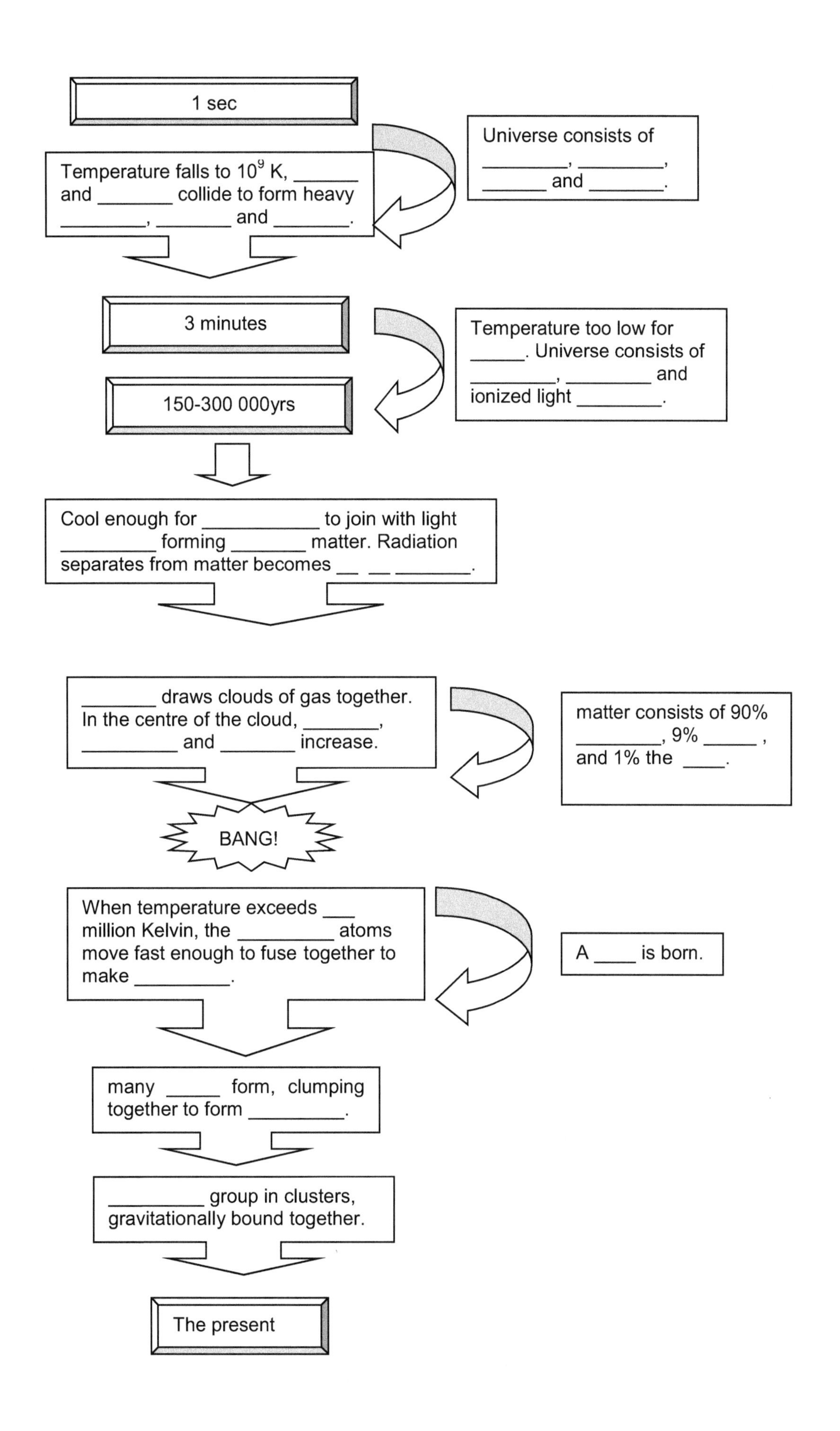
1 sec
Temperature falls to 10⁹ K, ______ and _______ collide to form heavy ________, _______ and _______.
Universe consists of ________, ________, ______ and _______.
3 minutes
150-300 000yrs
Temperature too low for _____. Universe consists of ________, ________ and ionized light ________.
Cool enough for ___________ to join with light _________ forming _______ matter. Radiation separates from matter becomes __ __ _______.
_______ draws clouds of gas together. In the centre of the cloud, _______, _________ and _______ increase.
matter consists of 90% ________, 9% ______ , and 1% the ____.
BANG!
When temperature exceeds ___ million Kelvin, the _________ atoms move fast enough to fuse together to make _________.
A ____ is born.
many _____ form, clumping together to form _________.
_________ group in clusters, gravitationally bound together.
The present

Exam Question Box 5: let's end with a big bang rather than a WIMPer. Fill in the missing words then check the answers on the next page.

The universe being (1) and isotropic is called the (2) principle. A graph of velocity against distance from galactic centre is called a (3). Near the centre, the velocity (4) with distance. Beyond a certain distance, the velocity is approximately (5). In theory the outer velocity should (6) with distance. The difference is caused by (7). Dark matter gives out (8) radiation and is gravitationally (9). (10) fluctuations in the (11) are of the order of (12). The increase in wavelength due to the expansion of space between galactic clusters is called the (13). (14) density is the density of the universe that will stop (15). Dark energy explains the (16) rate of (17) of the universe. Dark energy only interacts via (18). CSF stands for (19). When gravity separated from the other force, this is called (20). The sudden increase in the size of the universe that followed is called the (21).

D5 Answers

Task 26: anisotropic
Task 27: 174kms-1, 240 million yr. Use
v = √(G ρ 4π/3) x r with r in m then T = 2πr/v
Task 28: 190kms-1
2.6x1016s 830million years
Use v = √GM/r then
T = 2πr/v
about 250kms-1
1.9x1016s 610million years
Task 29: Cosmic Background Explorer.Wilkinson Microwave Anisotropy Project.
Task 30: 3.0
Task 31: About 33 billion years. Use ρc = 3H2÷8πG for H then T = 1/H.
Task 32: 0 would mean no expansion, -1 would mean a contraction

Exam Question 5 Answers:

1.homogeneous	2.cosmological	3.velocity curve	4.increases	5.constant
6.decrease	7.dark matter	8.no	9.attractive	10.temperature
11.cosmic microwave background	12. 10^{-4}K	13.cosmological redshift	14.critical	15.expansion
16.increasing	17.expansion	18.gravity	19.cosmic scale factor	20.symmetry breaking
21.Inflationary Epoch				

6 Common mistakes

- Units forgotten. Remember most quantities have units, e.g. luminosity in Watts, brightness in Watts metre^{-2} etc. Some have no units, e.g. z.
- Incorrect units are given. Remember units can be found from the equation, e.g. Hubble's constant H = v/d, v in kms^{-1} and D in Mpc, so units of Hubble's constant are kms^{-1}Mpc^{-1}.
- Quantities are not converted to the right units, e.g. wavelength in nanometres must normally be converted to metres.
- The answer is not rounded. Remember the guideline, round to the least number of digits given in the question.
- The temperature scale on an HR diagram is reversed. Remember temperature decreases from left to right on the diagram.
- A requested diagram is poorly drawn. Remember use a sharp pencil and a ruler! Such simple solutions gain valuable points.
- No working is shown. Remember that marks are given for working out and credit is possible even if the final answer is wrong.

7 Core Questions

D1.1a What is the largest planet is the solar system?
D1.1b What is the closest planet to the sun?
D1.1c Between which planets is the first asteroid belt found?
D1.1d From what are comets made?
D1.1e What is the name of an asymmetrical group of hundreds of stars bound together by gravity?
D1.1f What is the name of a spinning neutron star?
D1.1g What is the name of a gravitationally bound group of 1000 galaxies?
D1.2a What balances the force of gravity in a star and stops it collapsing?
D1.2b What do four hydrogen nuclei form under high temp and pressure?
D1.3a A galaxy is 6.0 x 10^{22} m away. How far is this in light years?
D1.3b The Beehive cluster is 520 ly away. What is this in metres?
D1.4a A star has a parallax of 0.43". What is the distance in parsecs? In light years? If the parallax error is +/-0.01" what is the distance error in pc?
D1.4b A star is 12pc away. What is its parallax?
D1.5a. A star has a surface temperature of 28 000K. What is the power output per unit area of surface?
D1.5b A star of luminosity 6.0x10^{28}W has a radius 3.0x10^{9} m. What is the surface temperature?
D1.5c A star of T = 15 000K has radius = 9.0 x 10^{8} m. What is the luminosity?
D1.5d. A star of luminosity 2.0 x 10^{26}W has a surface temperature 4000K. What is its radius?
D1.5e A star of luminosity 4.0 x 10^{27} W is observed from a distance of 2.0 x 10^{18} m. What is the apparent brightness?
D1.5f A star of apparent brightness 5.0 x 10^{-8} Wm^{-2} has a luminosity 3.2 x 10^{30} W. Find its distance.
D1.5g A star of apparent brightness 4.0 x 10^{-7} Wm^{-2} is known to be at a distance of 7.0 x 10^{19} m. What is its luminosity?
D2.1a A star's black body radiation curve peaks at a wavelength of 420nm. Find its surface temperature.
D2.1b Mira has a surface temperature of 3600K. At what wavelength does the black body radiation curve peak?
D2.1c Look at the black body radiation curves on page 8. Find the wavelength at maximum intensity for the middle curve and calculate the surface temperature.
D2.1d The black body radiation curve shown below was taken of the sun using the Go-Pro data logging system. By drawing a best fit curve, find the wavelength at peak intensity and hence the sun's surface temperature.

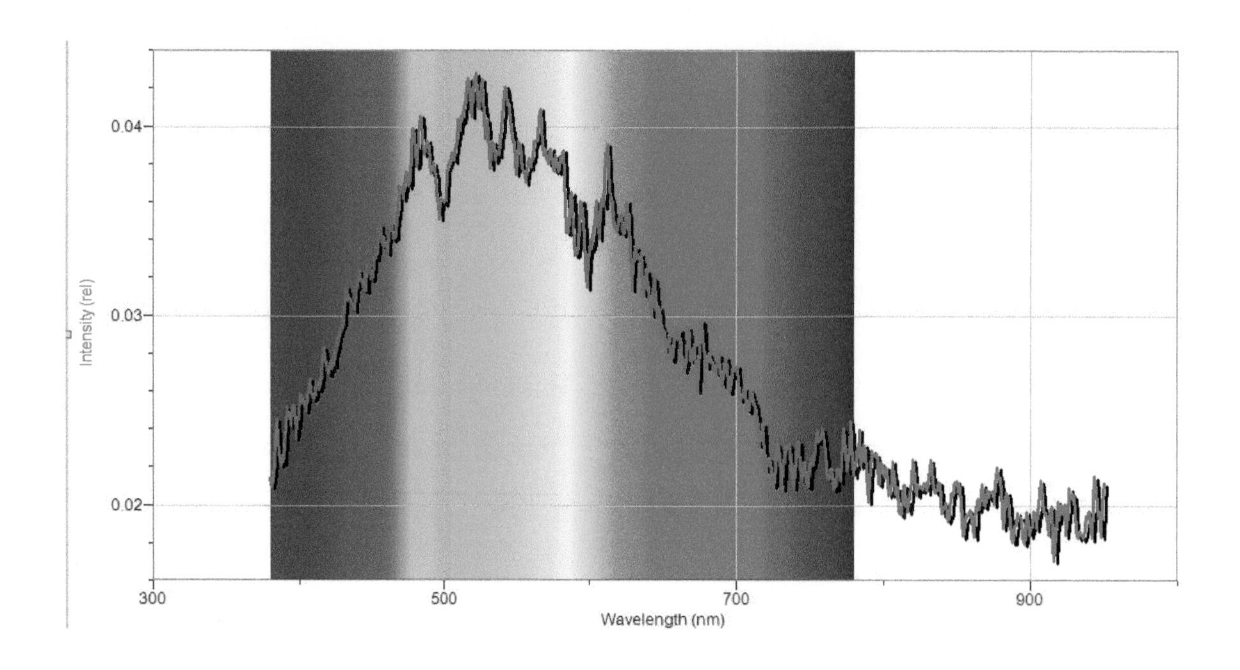

D2.2a A star is vertically above the sun on the HR diagram. What is different about the star? What is the same?
D2.2b A star is horizontally to the left of the sun on the HR diagram. What is different about the star? What is the same?
D2.3a A star is 137 times as luminous as the sun, what is its mass?
D2.3b A star has a mass $5M_{\odot}$, what is its luminosity?
D2.3c A star has a mass $0.5M_{\odot}$ and a brightness of $4.2 \times 10^{-8}Wm^{-2}$ how far away is it?
D2.4a A Cepheid variable has a brightness of $6.5 \times 10^{-9}Wm^{-2}$ and a period of 20days. Using the period luminosity graph on page 15 find its luminosity and distance.
D2.4b What causes the variation in Cepheids luminosity?
D2.4c Name the section on the HR diagram where Cepheids are found.
D2.5a Between which sections on the HR diagram are Cepheids found.
D2.5b Name the feature that comes after a nova, where the outer layers form a shell of gas round the star.
D2.5c After the sun leaves the giants on the HR diagram, where will it go?
D2.6a Use red giant RG, white dwarf WD, neutron star NS, black hole BH or pulsar PU to identify the following stars:

a strong off-axis magnetic field ...... : stops gravity by electron degeneracy .... : likely to be a strong X ray source ..... : many times the diameter of the sun .... : burning helium to carbon in its core .... : all the electrons pushed into the nuclei of its atoms .... : an escape velocity above that of light .... : detected by regular flashes in the visible and radio spectrum .... : of planetary size .... : this star has a surface temperature of about 3000K .....

D2.7a What is the $1.4M_{\odot}$ limit called?
D2.7b What is the $2.5M_{\odot}$ limit called?
D2.7c A star of mass $24M_{\odot}$ loses 90% in a supernova. What does the remaining mass become?
D2.7d Two stars of two solar mass each orbit one another and one draws 50% of the mass from the other. Assuming no other mass changes, what is the outcome of each star?
D3.1a Name the theory that states the universe began with an explosion.
D3.1b What is the universe expanding into?
D3.1c What is said about space and time before this explosion?
D3.2a What is the present temperature of the cosmic background radiation?
D3.2b Name the two scientists credited with discovering the CMB?
D3.2c If the CMB is at 2.6K, what is the wavelength at peak intensity?
D3.3a What is Hubble's Law?
D3.3b M51 has a recessional velocity of $350kms^{-1}$. If Hubble's constant is 78 $kms^{-1}Mpc^{-1}$ how far away is M51 in light years?
D3.3c When Hubble first tried to measure his constant he came up with the value of 500 $kms^{-1}Mpc^{-1}$. What would this value give for the age of the universe? The oldest rocks on the earth were known to be 4.7 billion years. What did Hubble's original constant imply from this?

D3.3d The hydrogen beta line has a wavelength of 432.00nm in the lab. When measured in the spectrum of the galaxy M31, the wavelength is 431.88nm. Find the velocity of the galaxy.
D3.3e A galaxy in the Virgo cluster has the hydrogen alpha line (wavelength 650.000nm) at 650.325 nm. Find the recessional velocity. From the Hubble law graph on page 26 find out how far away the galaxy is.
D3.3f A galaxy is 8Mpc away. Using Hubble's constant as $67kms^{-1}Mpc^{-1}$, find its recessional velocity. What will be the wavelength of the sodium line of 589.00nm?
D3.4a M86 emits a helium line (lab wavelength 612.3nm) with a wavelength of 613.7nm. What value of z does this give? What ratio does this give for R/Ro? What is the recessional velocity? Using the Hubble value of $78kms^{-1}$ Mpc^{-1} how far away is M86?
D3.4b What is happening to the expansion rate of the universe?
D3.4c What is causing this outcome?
D3.5a Suppose the present value of the cosmic scale factor is 1.21 that of the value from the galaxy M101 when the light we now see was created. What value does this give for z? What would be the wavelength of the sodium K line (589.1nm in the lab) and would it still be in the visible spectrum?
D3.5b the hydrogen line of wavelength 432nm in the lab is found to be 475nm in a distant galaxy. Find the recessional velocity. If H = $75kms^{-1}Mpc^{-1}$ find the distance.
D3.5c A type Ia supernova in the galaxy in the previous question reaches a brightness of $2.5x10^{-14}Wm^{-2}$. Type Ia are known to have a luminosity of $4.0 \times 10^{36}W$. What distance does this information give?
D4.1a Name three factors of a gas cloud that affects star formation.
D4.1b Arcturus has a mass of $10M_{\odot}$. How long did it stay on the main sequence compared to the sun's 10 billion yrs?
D4.1c If the universe is 14 billion yrs old, what would be the mass of a star that was created just after the Big Bang and is only now just leaving the main sequence?

D4.2a Fill in the missing symbols in the proton-proton chain below:
$H + ... \rightarrow D + e^+ + \nu + ...$
$... + H \rightarrow {}^3He + \gamma$
${}^3He + {}^3He \rightarrow .... + H + H + \gamma$
D4.2b In the CNO cycle below, fill in the missing symbols:
$H + {}^{12}C \rightarrow {}^{13}... + \gamma$
${}^{13}.... \rightarrow {}^{13}C + e^+ + ...$
$.... + {}^{13}C \rightarrow {}^{14}N + \gamma$
$H + {}^{14}N \rightarrow {}^{15}... + \gamma$
${}^{15}... \rightarrow {}^{15}N + ... + \nu$
$H + {}^{15}N \rightarrow {}^{12}C + ...$
D4.3a What is the s process?
D4.3b What is the r process?
D4.3c What is inverse beta decay?
D4.4a Which super nova has to be in a binary and what type of star must at least one of the stars be?
D4.4b Would a 5 solar mass star become a type II supernova?
D4.4c Would one see a type II supernova in an elliptical galaxy?

8 Higher level extension questions

D5.1a What is the cosmological principal?
D5.1b What does homogeneous mean?
D5.1c What does isotropic mean?
D5.2a What is a rotation curve?
D5.2b Sketch the rotation curve for the Milky Way.

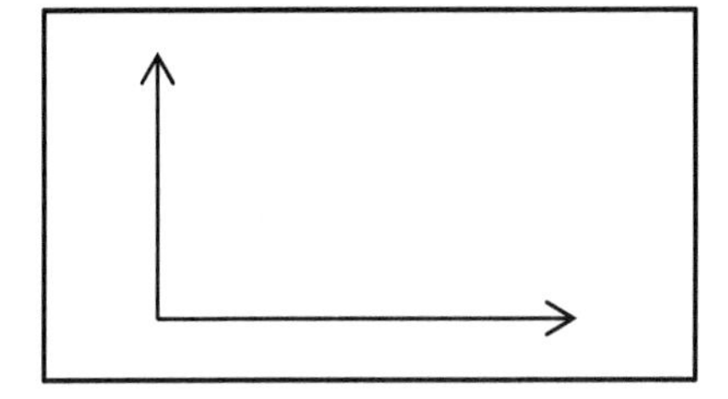

D5.2c Stars that are 10kpc from the centre of M31 and have a velocity of 300kms^{-1}. What density does this give for the galactic centre of M31? How many protons would this be equal to in a cubic metre?
D5.2d How is v and r related in the outer section?
D5.2e What cannot be explained by visible matter?
D5.3a What is dark matter?
D5.3b Where in the Milky Way is dark matter found?
D5.4a What does CMB stand for?
D5.4b What does the CMB say about the universe?
D5.4c When and with what project were anisotropies found in the CMB?
D5.4d What does anisotropy in the CMB mean?
D5.4e What do these anisotropies indicate about the universe?
D5.4f What is the present age of the universe?
D5.4g What is the accepted value of the Hubble Constant?
D5.5a How does cosmological redshift differ from local redshift?
D5.6a Define critical density.
D5.6b What is the critical density for a Hubble value of 68kms^{-1}Mpc^{-1}?
D5.6c How many protons per metre cubed would equal this density?
D5.7a What observation brought about the suggestion of dark energy?
D5.7b Give two properties of dark energy.
D5.7c What is the definition of the cosmic scale factor?
D5.7d What is the present scale factor and what does it imply?
D5.7e Sketch the graph of universe radius with time (see below).

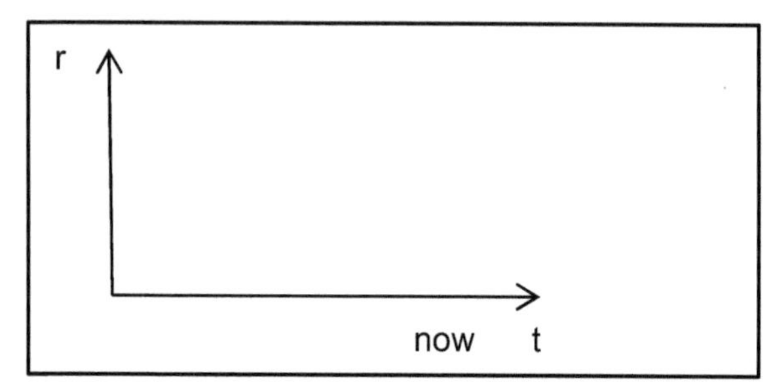

D5.7f How does the universe's temp depend on the cosmic scale factor?

9 Answers to Core Questions

(Note, clues are given in the brackets)

D1.1a Jupiter. D1.1b Mercury. D1.1c Mars and Jupiter. D1.1d ice and dust. D1.1e open (or moving) cluster. D1.1f pulsar. D1.1g supercluster. D1.2a radiation pressure. D1.2b helium. D1.3a 6.3 x 10^6 ly (use 1ly = 9.46 x 10^{15} m). D1.3b 4.9 x 10^{18} m. D1.4a 2.33+/- 0.05pc 7.6ly. D1.4b 0.083". D1.5a 3.5 x 10^{10} Wm^{-2} (use $L=\sigma AT^4$). D2.1a 6900K (use λ_{max} = 0.00290/T). D2.1b 8.1 x 10^{-7} m. D2.1c 5270K.D2.1d 520nm about 5600K D2.2a more luminous, same colour/surface temp. D2.2b hotter surface, same luminosity. D2.3a 4.1M$_\odot$ (use $L = M^{3.5}$) D2.3b 280L$_\odot$ D2.3c 0.85ly (a bit too close but 70 000yrs ago a red dwarf star did pass this close to the sun!) (0.088L$_\odot$ use sun's luminosity and $b=L/4\pi d^2$) D2.4a b = 6.9 x 10^{-9}Wm^{-2}, p = 20d.8000L so d = 650ly or 200pc D2.4b change in size leading to change in temperature and luminosity. D2.4c Instability strip. D2.5a main sequence and giant. D2.5b planetary nebula. D2.5c white dwarf. D2.6a PU, WD, BH, RG, RG, NS, BH, PU, WD, RG. D2.7a Chandrasakar limit. D2.7b Oppenhemer-Volkoff. D2.7c 2.4M$_\odot$ so a neutron star. D2.7d 1.5M$_\odot$ = neutron star, 0.5M$_\odot$ = white dwarf. D3.1a Big Bang. D3.1b nothing (not even a vacuum-not even nothing!). D3.1c there is no space and time before the explosion. D3.2a 2.76K. D3.2b Penzias and Wilson.D3.2c 0.0011m. D3.3a for a galaxy outside the local cluster recessional velocity proportional to distance. D3.3b 14.6 Mly D3.3c 2billion ly, earth is older than universe! D3.3d -83kms^{-1} i.e. towards us. D3.3e 150kms^{-1} = 3Mpc D3.3f 590.05nm. D3.4a z = 0.0023 R = 1.0023. D3.4b it is increasing. D3.4c dark energy. D3.5a z = 0.21, = 712.8nm in the red, yes. D3.5b 29 900kms^{-1} 398Mpc. D3.5c 380Mly. D4.1a mass, density, radius, temperature, (mean atomic mass). D4.1b 32 million years D4.1c 0.87M$_\odot$. D4.2a H or p, γ: D or ^{2}H: ^{4}He or α. D4.2b N: N, ν: O: O, e$^+$: ^{4}He or α. D4.3a slow (infrequent) neutron capture. D4.3b fast (often) neutron capture. D4.3c the capture of an electron by a proton to become a neutron. D4.4a type I. D4.4b no, min is 8M$_\odot$. D4.4c no, only spiral.

D5.1a universe is the same everywhere D5.1b uniform. D5.1c looks the same in all directions. D5.2a

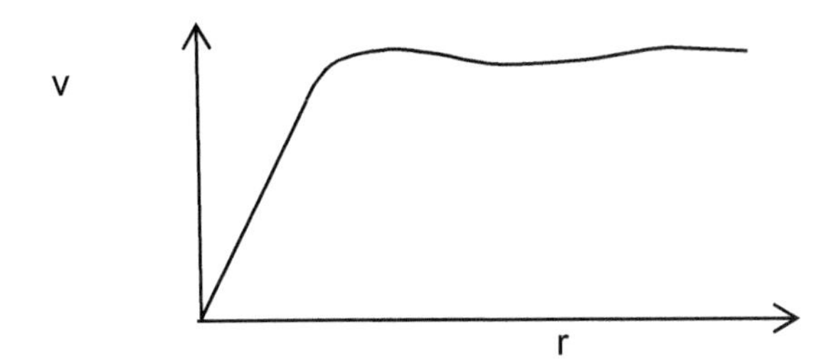

D5.2b v $\propto$ r near the centre. D5.2c 3.4 x 10^{-21}kgm^{-3} which is about 200 000 protons m^{-3}. D5.2d v is independent of radius in the outer section. D5.2e the outer velocity. D5.3a matter that is not seen as it gives out no radiation, only felt by gravity. D5.3b halo D5.4a cosmic microwave background. D5.4b an explosion occurred in the past-the cmb is radiation from this event. D5.4c COBE D5.4d slight differences in the CMB temperature in different directions. D5.4e it was slightly inhomogeneous (clumpy) D5.4f 13.8billion yr. D5.4g 77kms^{-1}Mpc^{-1} D5.5a local: radial motion of galaxies, cosmological: expansion of space. D5.6a density of universe to slow and eventually stop expansion. D5.6b 8.7 x 10^{-27}kgm^{-3}. D5.6c about 5 protons m^{-3}. D5.7a distant supernova shows expansion rate is speeding up. D5.7b gives out no radiation, repulsion with matter. D5.7c ratio of present expansion rate/rate at chosen point in past. D5.7d > 1, expansion rate increasing.
D5.7e Note dotted line shows the Inflationary Epoch.

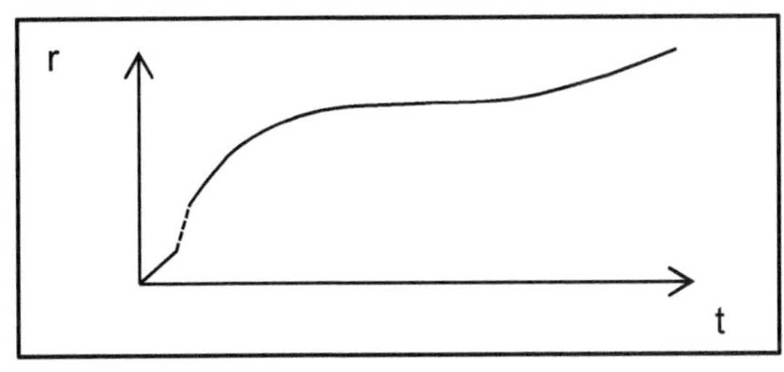

D5.7f T $\propto$ 1/R

The End

NOTES